Higher

History

Leckie✕Leckie

First exam published in 2003.
Published by Leckie & Leckie Ltd, 3rd Floor, 4 Queen Street, Edinburgh EH2 1JE
tel: 0131 220 6831 fax: 0131 225 9987 enquiries@leckieandleckie.co.uk www.leckieandleckie.co.uk

ISBN 1-84372-443-X   ISBN-13 978-1-84372-443-8

A CIP Catalogue record for this book is available from the British Library.

Printed in Scotland by Scotprint.

Leckie & Leckie is a division of Granada Learning Limited.

Leckie & Leckie is grateful to the copyright holders, as credited at the back of the book, for permission to use their material. Every effort has been made to trace the copyright holders and to obtain their permission for the use of copyright material. Leckie & Leckie will gladly receive information enabling them to rectify any error or omission in subsequent editions.

2003 | Higher

[BLANK PAGE]

X044/301

NATIONAL
QUALIFICATIONS
2003

TUESDAY, 20 MAY
1.00 PM – 2.20 PM

HISTORY
HIGHER
Paper 1

Answer questions on **one** Option only.

Take particular care to show clearly the Option chosen. On the **front** of the answer book, **in the top right-hand corner**, write A or B or C.

Within the Option chosen, answer **two** questions, one from Historical Study: Scottish and British and one from Historical Study: European and World.

All questions are assigned 25 marks.

Marks may be deducted for bad spelling and bad punctuation, and for writing that is difficult to read.

(Remember that you will have to choose in Paper 2 a Special Topic from the Option on which you answer questions in Paper 1.)

SCOTTISH
QUALIFICATIONS
AUTHORITY

©

[BLANK PAGE]

OPTION A: MEDIEVAL HISTORY

**Answer TWO questions, one from Historical Study: Scottish and British
and one from Historical Study: European and World.**

Historical Study: Scottish and British

Medieval Society

1. How effective was twelfth-century feudalism as a system of government?

2. How important were royal burghs in the society of twelfth-century England and Scotland?

3. How far did the twelfth-century Church rely on religious belief for its power?

4. "David I's success as king of Scotland was due to his arriving with powerful friends." To what extent do you agree?

5. "Henry II's reform of the justice system was the main reason for the increase in royal power during his reign." Discuss.

Historical Study: European and World

EITHER

Nation and King

6. How far was Magna Carta the result of efforts by King John of England to reduce the power of the barons?

7. Compare the contributions of Philip II and Louis IX to the growth of the French monarchy.

8. "The Wars of Independence were of vital importance in creating a Scottish national identity." Discuss.

9. Why did Scotland win the Wars of Independence?

OR

Crisis of Authority

10. How important was the role played by Joan of Arc in bringing about the French victory in the Hundred Years' War?

11. What was the main reason for the decline of serfdom in the fourteenth century?

12. To what extent were national rivalries a serious problem for the Church during the fourteenth and early fifteenth centuries?

13. "Medieval society was in political, religious and economic decline by the fifteenth century." Discuss.

OPTION B: EARLY MODERN HISTORY

Answer TWO questions, one from Historical Study: Scottish and British and one from Historical Study: European and World.

Historical Study: Scottish and British

EITHER

Scotland in the Age of the Reformation 1542–1603

1. "The success of the Reformation in Scotland owed more to the weaknesses of the Roman Catholic Church than to the reformers." How far do you agree?

2. To what extent was the Scottish Reformation a radical break with the past?

3. Why did Mary, Queen of Scots, have such a difficult time ruling Scotland?

4. "James VI's conflict with Andrew Melville was as much political as religious." Discuss.

5. How important a part did the nobility play in the political life of Scotland between 1542 and 1603?

OR

Scotland and England in the Century of Revolutions 1603–1702

6. How successfully did James VI deal with the problems that faced him as an absentee king of Scotland after 1603?

7. Assess the importance of financial issues in damaging relations between Crown and Parliament in England between 1603 and 1640.

8. To what extent do you agree that civil war had become inevitable in England by 1642?

9. "The Protectorate failed because it was based on religious beliefs, not political ideas." How far do you agree?

10. To what extent was the Revolution of 1688–1689 a significant turning point in English and Scottish history?

Historical Study: European and World

EITHER

Royal Authority in 17th and 18th Century Europe

11. How far did the position of the nobility change in France during the reign of Louis XIV?

12. Why was Colbert unable to solve the financial problems of the French state?

13. To what extent is it true that Frederick II of Prussia was a more enlightened ruler than Joseph II of Austria?

14. How successful were the social reforms of Joseph II?

OR

The French Revolution: The Emergence of the Citizen State

15. "The grievances of the bourgeoisie were more of a threat to the Ancien Regime than the grievances of the peasantry." How far do you agree?

16. To what extent was Louis XVI responsible for the outbreak of the French Revolution?

17. How effective was government under the French National Assembly (1789–1794)?

18. What was the most important reason for the failure to establish stable government in France by 1799?

[Turn over

OPTION C: LATER MODERN HISTORY

**Answer TWO questions, one from Historical Study: Scottish and British
and one from Historical Study: European and World.**

Historical Study: Scottish and British

Britain 1850s–1979

1. What was the most important reason for the growth of democracy in Britain between 1867 and 1928?

2. To what extent did the Liberal Reforms (1906–1914) improve the lives of the British people?

3. How great an impact did the labour movement have on Britain by 1922?

4. How effectively did the policies of the National Government deal with the problem of mass unemployment in Britain in the 1930s?

5. **Either**

   (a) To what extent were changes in Scottish leisure, religion and education between 1880 and 1939 due to urbanisation?

   Or

   (b) Is it fair to dismiss electoral support for the Scottish National Party as simply a protest vote?

Historical Study: European and World

EITHER

The Growth of Nationalism

6. **Either**

   (*a*) To what extent was there a real growth of national consciousness in Germany between 1815 and 1850?

   Or

   (*b*) How far was the growth in Italian nationalism between 1815 and 1850 due to the work of Mazzini?

7. **Either**

   (*a*) How important was Prussian military strength in the unification of Germany by 1871?

   Or

   (*b*) "Italy will do it herself." (King Charles Albert of Piedmont) How far did the process of unification justify this claim?

8. **Either**

   (*a*) "Propaganda was crucial to the Nazi rise to power in Germany between 1919 and 1933." How far do you agree?

   Or

   (*b*) How important was Mussolini himself in the rise to power of the Fascists in Italy by 1922?

9. **Either**

   (*a*) Assess the impact of Nazi rule on the people of Germany between 1933 and 1939.

   Or

   (*b*) Assess the impact of Fascist rule on the people of Italy between 1922 and 1939.

[Turn over

Historical Study: European and World

OR

The Large Scale State

The USA

10. Why did the United States become increasingly hostile towards immigration during the 1920s?

11. "Despite success on the surface, serious problems and inequalities remained." How far do you accept this view of Republican economic policies in the 1920s?

12. "Its role in recovery from the Depression was very limited." To what extent do you accept this view of the New Deal?

13. Why did the civil rights movement gain so much support in the 1950s and early 1960s?

Russia

14. How significant was military power in maintaining the authority of the Tsarist state in the years before 1905?

15. How important was social suffering in causing the revolution of 1905?

16. Why did the authority of the Tsarist state collapse so completely in 1917?

17. How far was the success of the Bolsheviks in the Civil War due to divisions among their opponents?

[END OF QUESTION PAPER]

X044/302

NATIONAL QUALIFICATIONS 2003	TUESDAY, 20 MAY 2.40 PM – 4.05 PM	**HISTORY HIGHER** Paper 2

Answer questions on only **one** Special Topic which should be from the Option on which you answered questions in Paper 1.

Take particular care to show clearly the Special Topic chosen. On the **front** of the answer book, **in the top right-hand corner**, write the number of the Special Topic.

You are expected to use background knowledge appropriately in answering source-based questions.

Marks may be deducted for bad spelling and bad punctuation, and for writing that is difficult to read.

Some sources have been adapted or translated.

SCOTTISH
QUALIFICATIONS
AUTHORITY

[BLANK PAGE]

OPTION A: MEDIEVAL HISTORY

SPECIAL TOPIC 1: NORMAN CONQUEST AND EXPANSION 1050–1153

Study the sources below and then answer the questions which follow.

Source A: from *The Deeds of William, Duke of the Normans and King of the English* written about 1071 by William of Poitiers.

William went to different parts of the kingdom, arranging everything to his satisfaction and that of the inhabitants. Wherever he went all laid down their arms. There was no resistance, but everywhere men submitted to him or sought his peace . . . The atheling [Edgar] himself, whom after the fall of Harold the English thought to make king, he gave wide lands and took into the closest circle of his affection because he was of the race of King Edward, and also so that the boy in his youth should not too bitterly regret the loss of the honour to which he had once been chosen. Many English received his [William's] liberal gift more than they had ever from their fathers or their former lords. He placed capable castellans with ample forces of horse and foot in his castles, men brought over from France in whose loyalty he could trust. He gave them rich fiefs in return for which they willingly endured hardship and danger. But to no Frenchman was anything given unjustly taken from an Englishman.

Source B: from Brian Golding, *Conquest and Colonisation* (1994).

We know that the English aristocracy all but disappeared, but how that happened remains unclear. How brutal were the confiscations? What happened to the disinherited? Occasionally Domesday sheds some dim light on the process. Azor, a steward of Edward the Confessor, had a small estate which William granted to him at Windsor, but Robert d'Oilly seized it unjustly. Here the realities of Conquest at local level replaced legitimacy. The experience of Ailric, a free tenant in 1066, but who held his lands of a new Norman lord in 1086 for rent, "harshly and wretchedly", is well known. Domesday also tells how in Essex a free man who had held half a hide was "now become one of the villeins". The thegn, Cheping, held lands in Hampshire valued at £127 in 1066. All of his estates had passed to Ralph de Mortimer by 1086. In general it would seem that the more prosperous native landholders lost all or most of their lands, while lesser men were more likely to be able to retain theirs—but at a price.

Source C: from a letter from Pope Gregory VII to Hubert, subdeacon of the Roman Church in England (23 September 1079).

Gregory, the bishop, servant of the servants of God, to his dear son in Christ, Hubert . . . you have informed us that Tenzo, as legate on our behalf, has spoken against the King of England [William]. This, you should know, is not by our command. Nevertheless, the Roman Church has many things whereof to complain against William. For none of all the kings, not excepting those that are heathen, has dared to act against the Church in the way he has unblushingly done. None has been so irreverent or shameless as to forbid the bishops and archbishops to visit the Pope. Wherefore, we would have you warn him on our behalf not to strive so ardently to diminish the honour of the holy Roman Church . . .

Source D: from the Ecclesiastical History of Orderic Vitalis, written between c. 1114 and 1141.

At this time Swein King of Denmark fitted out a great fleet of Danes and English and sent it to England. He had received many messengers from the English begging for help and had a desire for the kingdom to which he had a claim of inheritance . . . The Danes reached York, and a general rising of the inhabitants swelled their ranks. The garrison made a rash sally to attack them and engaged them ill-advisedly within the city walls. Unable to resist such numbers they were all slain or taken prisoner . . . About this time the West Saxons of Dorset and Somerset with their neighbours attacked Montacute, but by the will of God failed to take it. The Welshmen and men of Chester besieged the royal stronghold at Shrewsbury, and were assisted by the native citizens, the powerful and warlike Edric the Wild, and other untameable Englishmen. The men of Devon were attacking Exeter in the same way, allied with the hordes from Cornwall.

Source E: from R. A. Brown, *The Normans and the Norman Conquest* (1985).

The Normans of the eleventh century excelled in the art of war. Warfare at this time was increasingly dominated by heavy cavalry and castles, and in the use of both it is evident that the Normans were at the forefront of developments. Normandy in 1066 was full of knights and had indeed been "exporting" them, especially as younger sons, for over a generation, to Spain, Italy and beyond. At Hastings, knights were the heavy cavalry, whose hauberk distinguished them from lesser men, and in society at large they were the ruling class.

[END OF SOURCES FOR SPECIAL TOPIC 1]

SPECIAL TOPIC 1: NORMAN CONQUEST AND EXPANSION 1050–1153

Answer *all* of the following questions.

Marks

1. How valuable is **Source A** as evidence of the treatment of English nobles after the Conquest?

   In reaching a conclusion you should refer to:
   • *the origin and possible purpose of the source;*
   • *the content of the source;*
   • *recalled knowledge.* **4**

2. Compare the views of **Sources A** and **B** on the treatment of English people by the Normans.

   Compare the content overall and in detail. **5**

3. How far do you accept the views in **Source C** about William's impact on the English church and nobility?

   Use the source and recalled knowledge. **6**

4. How secure was the new regime in England under William the Conqueror?

   *Use **Sources A, C** and **D** and recalled knowledge.* **8**

5. How fully does **Source E** explain the reasons for Norman expansion in the 11th century?

   Use the source and recalled knowledge. **7**

   (30)

[END OF QUESTIONS ON SPECIAL TOPIC 1]

SPECIAL TOPIC 2: THE CRUSADES 1096–1204

Study the sources below and then answer the questions which follow.

Source A: from *The Deeds of God through the Franks*, by Guibert, abbot of Nogent in France, written between 1105 and 1109.

Baldwin soon arrived to besiege Tarsus, set up camp on the other side, and asked Tancred if he and his army might share in the taking of the city. Tancred angrily refused, since he wanted control of the city and the trophies of victory for himself alone.

[The city surrendered and] Baldwin instantly urged Tancred that they enter the city together, so that each might set about taking the spoils with all his might. Tancred wisely replied, "Our plan was to fight the Turks, not to rob the Christians".

[Later Baldwin became the new ruler of Edessa and put down two uprisings.] And so, after the leaders of the entire city had been convicted, some had their feet cut off, some their hands, others their ears and noses, others their tongues and lips, and all of them were castrated and sent into exile in various distant places. Finally, when no-one remained who might incite the crowd against him, Baldwin experienced the rewards and happiness of such a dukedom. Thereafter he led a prosperous and rich life and ruled several cities.

Source B: the defeat of Kerbogha at Antioch, from the *Deeds of the Franks*, written c. 1100.

At last, after three days spent in fasting and in processions from one church to another, our men confessed their sins and received absolution . . . Then six lines of battle were drawn up from those who were in the city . . . So we closed our ranks, and protected by the Sign of the Cross we went out by the gate which is over against the mosque.

Then also appeared from the mountains a countless host of men on white horses, whose banners were all white . . . This is quite true, for many of our men saw it.

Then we called upon the true and living God and rode against them, joining battle in the name of Jesus Christ and of the Holy Sepulchre, and by God's help we defeated them.

The Turks fled in terror and we pursued them right up to their camp, for the knights of Christ were more eager to chase them than to look for any plunder.

Source C: from A. Maalouf, *The Crusades Through Arab Eyes* (1983).

The strong man of Cairo, vizier al-Afdal, had not concealed his satisfaction when, in April 1097, ambassadors from Alexius Comnenus had informed him that a massive contingent of Frankish knights had arrived in Constantinople and were about to launch an offensive in Asia Minor.

Since the middle of the century, Seljuk advances had been eroding the territory of the Fatimid caliphate and the Byzantine empire alike. Al-Afdal dreamed of a concerted operation by the two allied powers, and when he learned that the emperor had received a large reinforcement of troops from the lands of the Franks, he felt that revenge was at hand.

The delegation he dispatched to the besiegers of Antioch made no mention of a non-aggression pact. That much was obvious, thought the vizier. What he proposed to the Franks was a formal partition: northern Syria for the Franks, southern Syria (meaning Palestine, Damascus and the coastal cities as far north as Beirut) for him.

Source D: from the *Itinerary of Richard I*, written in the early thirteenth century.

The king's illness had now become so extremely serious that he despaired of ever recovering his health. He was very anxious about this, as much for others as for himself. His astute mind considered many options but his preferred choice, the least disagreeable, was to demand a truce. The alternative would be to depart, leaving the campaign unfinished, and abandon the country altogether to depopulation, as all the others had done who were already leaving in hordes by ship.

So, perplexed and not knowing what else to do, the king sent a message to Saladin's brother Saphadin, asking for him to mediate and obtain a truce between them on the most honourable conditions that he could.

Source E: from T. Jones and A. Ereira, *The Crusades* (1996).

Richard's chroniclers saw what followed [at Jaffa in 1192] as a heroic battle, a marvellous vision of Richard the perfect warrior in action, triumphant against overwhelming odds.

In fact, what happened was not quite like that. Although the Mamelukes (slave warriors from Egypt) had charged and been seen off by the crossbowmen, the rest of Saladin's troops had mutinied. Saladin was told that since he had confiscated their booty—presumably for the enrichment of his own family—he should go and fight for himself. They had had enough.

The energy of the *jihad* had evaporated with the conquest of Jerusalem, and Saladin's moment in history was past. Back in 1098 at Antioch, victory against equally impossible odds had been achieved when the Turks similarly refused to fight for their commander. Then, victory had been ascribed to divine intervention. Now, almost a hundred years later, it was ascribed to the hero. God was no longer needed. The energy of the Holy War had evaporated on the Christian side as much as on the Muslim.

[END OF SOURCES FOR SPECIAL TOPIC 2]

SPECIAL TOPIC 2: THE CRUSADES 1096–1204

Answer *all* of the following questions.   *Marks*

1. Compare the motives of the crusaders as shown by **Sources A** and **B**.
    Compare the content overall and in detail.   **5**

2. How typical were Baldwin and Tancred as leaders of the First Crusade? Refer to **Source A** and your own knowledge.
    Use the source and recalled knowledge.   **6**

3. How fully does Maalouf (**Source C**) illustrate the weaknesses of the Muslims during the First Crusade?
    Use the source and recalled knowledge.   **6**

4. How valuable is **Source D** as evidence of King Richard's reasons for negotiating a truce with Saladin at the end of the Third Crusade?
    In reaching a conclusion you should refer to:
    *   *the origin and possible bias of the source;*
    *   *the content of the source;*
    *   *recalled knowledge.*   **5**

5. How far do **Sources B**, **D** and **E** support the view that the idea of the Crusade as a holy war became less important between the 11th and 13th centuries?
    *Refer to **Sources B, D** and **E** and recalled knowledge.*   **8**

                                                                                                              (30)

[END OF QUESTIONS ON SPECIAL TOPIC 2]

OPTION B: EARLY MODERN HISTORY

SPECIAL TOPIC 3: SCOTLAND 1689–1715

Study the sources below and then answer the questions which follow.

Source A: from Queen Anne's instructions to the Earl of Seafield, April 1704.

Instructions to our right trusty and right well-beloved cousin and counsellor, James, Earl of Seafield, our Chancellor.

You are to go to Scotland without loss of time and there make known our pleasure that we are fully resolved to do all that we can to have the succession settled, failing heirs of our body, on Princess Sophia of Hanover and the heirs of her body. We will employ none in our service but people who will concur in so necessary and so good a work.

Source B: from a petition from Stirling Town Council against the proposed incorporating union, 18 November 1706.

We desire that true peace and friendship be always cultivated with our neighbour in England, upon just and honourable terms . . . Yet we judge that going into this Treaty will bring an insupportable burden of taxation upon this land, which freedom of trade will never repay . . . [Scotland would still be] under the regulations of the English in the Parliament of Britain, who may if they please discourage the most valuable branches of our trade, if any way seen to interfere with their own. It will ruin our manufactories, our religion, laws and liberties and deprive the royal burghs, of our fundamental right of being represented in the legislative power.

We therefore . . . firmly expect that ye will not conclude an incorporating union so destructive to many and dangerous to the whole of these things which are dear to us.

Source C: from a speech in Parliament on the First Article of the Treaty of Union, 1706, William Seton of Pitmedden.

These queries ought to be duly examined . . . whether any federal union betwixt England and Scotland is sufficient to secure the peace of this island, or fortify it against the intrigues and invasions of its foreign enemies? And whether it should be wise for England to give its trade and protection to this nation till both kingdoms are incorporated into one?

I could give some account of the particular advantages we'll obtain by an incorporating union with England. In general, I may assert, that by this union we'll have access to all the advantages of commerce the English enjoy. We'll be able to improve our national product for the benefit of the whole island. We'll have our liberty, property and religion secured under the protection of one sovereign and one Parliament of Great Britain.

Source D: from W. Ferguson, *Scotland's Relations with England: A survey to 1707* (1977).

The Treaty's easy passage through the English Parliament showed that, quite apart from masterly management, there was no great opposition to it there. Of all the remarkable changes of the time this was the most remarkable. At the beginning of Anne's reign there had been strong aversion in England to the idea of union with Scotland, but by 1707 it was English insistence that made union possible. There is no mystery about what caused this change of attitude—it was brought about by fears for the security of England. A disgruntled Scotland raised the spectre of French intervention and of attack from the north.

Source E: from T. M. Devine, *The Scottish Nation 1700–2000* (1999).

A long and rocky road had to be travelled after 1707 before the new relationship between the two countries was finally formalised, and at some points along this difficult route the very survival of the new union was sometimes in grave doubt.

There was the continuing Jacobite threat . . . Jacobites were completely opposed to the union since they viewed it—correctly—as a means of making permanent the Revolution of 1688–1689 and so ensuring that the Stuarts would never again return to their rightful inheritance.

In 1710 the High Church Tories seemed bent on a policy of removing the privileges of the Church of Scotland guaranteed in the Treaty of Union . . . The decision to allow the Anglican prayer book to be used for worship in an Episcopalian meeting house enraged the capital's Presbyterians.

[In 1713] Scottish peers and members of the Commons came together in a series of meetings and agreed that the only solution was repeal of the treaty. The motion was put to the House of Lords in June 1713 and was only narrowly defeated by four votes.

[END OF SOURCES FOR SPECIAL TOPIC 3]

SPECIAL TOPIC 3: SCOTLAND 1689–1715

Answer *all* of the following questions.

Marks

1. How fully does **Source A** explain why relations between Scotland and England deteriorated between 1690 and 1705?

   Use the source and recalled knowledge.　　　**6**

2. How useful is **Source B** as evidence of Scottish attitudes to Union?

   In reaching a conclusion you should refer to:
   * *the origin and possible purpose of the source;*
   * *the content of the source;*
   * *recalled knowledge.*　　　**4**

3. Compare the different points of view in **Sources B** and **C** on the advantages of an incorporating union.

   Compare the content overall and in detail.　　　**6**

4. To what extent do **Sources A**, **C** and **D** identify the factors which led to the passing of the Act of Union?

   *Use **Sources A, C** and **D** and recalled knowledge.*　　　**8**

5. How adequate is the explanation given in **Source E** for the attempt to dissolve the Union in 1713?

   Use the source and recalled knowledge.　　　**6**

   (30)

[END OF QUESTIONS ON SPECIAL TOPIC 3]

SPECIAL TOPIC 4: THE ATLANTIC SLAVE TRADE

Study the sources below and then answer the questions which follow.

Source A: from a pamphlet reporting a speech made by Wilberforce in the House of Commons, 12 May 1789.

The description of their ship was impossible, so much misery confined in so little room, so much affliction added to misery . . . Six hundred slaves linked together, trying to get rid of each other, and crammed in a close vessel, with every object that was nauseous and disgusting; with pestilence, disease and despair . . . Yet, shocking as this description must be felt to be by every man, it had been described by several witnesses from Liverpool as comfortable.

[We have heard] Mr Norris describe the accommodation of a slave ship in the most favourable terms; instruments of music were employed to amuse them; the song and the dance were promoted . . . But the way the song and the dance were promoted was by severe whipping, when the poor wretches would not take any voluntary exercise!

Source B: from a Circular Letter of the London Abolition Committee, June 1787.

We are not without hopes of this trade becoming a subject of Parliamentary investigation early in the next session. If that should be the case, it is to be wished that the general sense of the nation (which we are persuaded is in favour of liberty, justice and humanity) may be expressed by petitions to Parliament, and by applications to their representatives, in order to procure their assistance. In the distribution of the enclosed tracts, we therefore recommend this purpose may be kept in view.

Source C: from P. E. H. Hair, *The Atlantic Slave Trade and Black Africa* (1978).

On the European side, economic gain was the prime motive of trade with Black Africa, as of any other trade. For most of the businessmen concerned, profits arose—hopefully—from the overall transactions during "triangular" voyages from Europe to Europe, via Africa and America. Profits solely from trade in slaves were rarely distinguishable in such records as were kept. The return on the investment in a specific voyage ranged from a bonanza gain to total loss of the capital (caused by slave insurrection, war seizure or marine disaster—the last two not uncommon happenings). In fact it often fluctuated wildly from voyage to voyage.

Source D: from Samuel Taylor Coleridge, *On the Slave Trade* (1796).

It is my present purpose to consider the objections to the abolition of this commerce.

One objection is that the Revenue would be damaged.

However, it seems to have been proved, that the West-India trade is more often a losing than a winning trade—a lottery with more blanks than prizes in it. It is likewise asserted to be the grave of our seamen. This objection, therefore, ought not to have been made, till these doubts had been cleared up.

Source E: from R. Anstey, *The Atlantic Slave Trade and British Abolition, 1760–1810* (1975).

The immediate explanation of the passage of the 1807 bill lies in systematic abolitionist lobbying, and, much more importantly, political pressure . . . A significant shift of opinion had already taken place by the middle of 1806. Stephen's* masterly tactic of concentrating first on the abolition of those branches of the trade which could be represented as harming the national interest in time of war, meant that the political nation was confronted all of a sudden with the fact that it had abolished what was believed to be nearly two-thirds of the British Slave Trade almost without realising it.

Twenty years elapsed between the foundation of the London Abolition Committee and the final accomplishment of its object. Such a delay shows that general support in the country was not enough to secure abolition. It was as a political campaign that abolition had to succeed, for it was only by means of the political process that pressure on parliament could lead to the necessary legislation. As a pressure group the abolitionists were, for their day, unique. Their leadership was outstanding and their organisation was impressive . . . They fought hard and in the end with success, as the 1807 bill was based openly on justice and humanity, but most of the trade had already been stopped for other reasons.

* Stephen was William Wilberforce's brother-in-law and a member of the abolitionist committee.

[END OF SOURCES FOR SPECIAL TOPIC 4]

SPECIAL TOPIC 4: THE ATLANTIC SLAVE TRADE

Answer *all* of the following questions.   *Marks*

1. How accurate is Wilberforce's description (**Source A**) of conditions suffered by the slaves on the Middle Passage?

   Use the source and recalled knowledge.   **6**

2. How valuable is **Source B** as evidence of the tactics used by abolitionists?

   In reaching a conclusion you should refer to:
   * *the origin and possible purpose of the source;*
   * *the content of the source;*
   * *recalled knowledge.*   **5**

3. To what extent does **Source D** support the evidence in **Source C** on the value of the slave trade?

   Compare the content overall and in detail.   **5**

4. How adequate is the explanation given in **Source E** for the eventual abolition of the slave trade?

   Use the source and recalled knowledge.   **6**

5. How fully do **Sources B, D** and **E** reflect the issues in the debate over the slave trade?

   *Use **Sources B, D** and **E** and recalled knowledge.*   **8**

                                                                                               (30)

[END OF QUESTIONS ON SPECIAL TOPIC 4]

SPECIAL TOPIC 5: THE AMERICAN REVOLUTION

Study the sources below and then answer the questions which follow.

Source A: from a speech in Parliament by Lord North introducing the Coercive Acts, 1774.

The Americans have tarred and feathered your Majesty's subjects, plundered your merchants, burnt your ships, denied all obedience to your laws and authority. Yet our conduct for so long has been patient. It is essential that we take a different course. Whatever may be the consequence we must risk something; if we do not, all is lost.

Source B: from the Declaration of Causes of Taking up Arms, Continental Congress, 1775.

They have undertaken to give and grant our money without our consent, though we have always exercised an exclusive right to dispose of our own property. Laws have been passed to extend the jurisdiction of courts of Admiralty and Vice-Admiralty beyond their ancient limits; to deprive us of the accustomed and vital privilege of trial by jury, in cases affecting both life and property; to suspend the legislature of one of the colonies; . . . to set up in a neighbouring province, acquired by the joint arms of Great Britain and America, a despotism dangerous to our very existence; and to quarter soldiers upon the colonists in time of peace.

Source C: from the Declaration of Independence, 1776.

The history of the present King of Great Britain is a history of repeated injuries, all having in direct object the establishment of an absolute tyranny over these states. He has combined with others to subject us to a government foreign to our constitution, giving his assent to their acts of pretended legislation;

> For quartering large bodies of armed troops among us:
> For cutting off our trade with all parts of the world:
> For imposing taxes on us without our consent:
> For depriving us, in many cases of the benefits of trial by jury: . . .

In every state of these oppressions we have petitioned for redress in the most humble terms; our repeated petitions have been answered only by repeated injury. A king whose character is marked by every act as a tyrant is unfit to be ruler of a free people.

Source D: from I. R. Christie, *Crisis of Empire* (1966).

The ministers at home failed to understand the urgency, mainly because they consistently underestimated the extent of rebel sentiment and overestimated the strength of the loyalists. And even had they grasped it, the senior British military commanders were not the men to respond. In fighting spirit they were far inferior to the American officers who opposed them. The consequences of mismanagement were fatal. British and loyalist morale gradually fell while that of the rebels rose.

Source E: from a letter from Washington to Reverend William Gordon, July 1783.

Unless adequate powers are given to Congress for the general purposes of the Federal Union we shall soon become ridiculous in the eyes of Europe . . . We are known as the United States.

Why does Congress spend months together in deliberating upon, debating and digesting plans . . . when some States will pay little or no attention to them; . . . I think the blood and treasure which has been spent in this war has been lavished to little purpose unless we can be better cemented. That will not happen while so little attention is paid to the recommendations of the Congress.

For heaven's sake who are Congress? Are they not the creatures of the people? Where can be the danger of giving them such powers as are necessary for government and for all the general purposes of the Confederation?

[END OF SOURCES FOR SPECIAL TOPIC 5]

SPECIAL TOPIC 5: THE AMERICAN REVOLUTION

Answer *all* of the following questions. *Marks*

1. How valuable is **Source A** as evidence of British policy towards America in the years before the outbreak of war?

   In reaching a conclusion you should refer to:
   * *the origin and possible purpose of the source;*
   * *the content of the source;*
   * *recalled knowledge.*   5

2. To what extent does **Source C** confirm the colonists' attitude to Britain expressed in **Source B**?

   Compare the content overall and in detail.   5

3. How fully do **Sources A**, **B** and **C** identify the issues which led to the breakdown of relations between Britain and her American colonies?

   *Use **Sources A, B** and **C** and recalled knowledge.*   8

4. How important were the reasons given in **Source D** in explaining Britain's defeat in the American War of Independence?

   Use the source and recalled knowledge.   6

5. To what extent did the 1787 Constitution address the issues outlined in **Source E**?

   Use the source and recalled knowledge.   6

       (30)

[END OF QUESTIONS ON SPECIAL TOPIC 5]

OPTION C: LATER MODERN HISTORY

SPECIAL TOPIC 6: PATTERNS OF MIGRATION: SCOTLAND 1830s–1930s

Study the sources below and then answer the questions which follow.

Source A: from the *Report of the State of the Irish Poor in Great Britain* (1836). Evidence of Mr Houndsworth, cotton manufacturer, Glasgow.

Wages in the spinning department of the cotton trade have been kept down by the Irish, or rather they have been prevented from rising. In handloom weaving the Irish have lowered wages, partly from their competition for work with our native weavers, but more particularly as without them the power-loom could not, from want of hands, have made the progress it has. I do not think the manufacturer could afford to give higher wages to weavers than the present rate. Nothing can raise weavers' wages to their former level without injuring the trade. The prices do not admit of an advance of wages.

Source B: from C. A. Whatley, *The Industrial Revolution in Scotland* (1997).

Prepared to accept lower wages, the Irish tended to be drawn into easier-to-enter trades such as handloom weaving, where they accounted for around 30% of the workforce by the later 1830s. They were used by employers who exploited the opportunities their presence provided to introduce "blackleg" labour into coal mines for example, or do the more burdensome jobs such as ironstone mining, along with certain unskilled work where they were more numerous than the Scots. Resentment on the part of those sections of the native population who felt the direct effects of low-wage competition and the fact that the religion of the majority of the immigrants was Roman Catholicism heightened social tensions in mining and weaving towns and villages in Presbyterian counties such as Lanarkshire and Ayrshire; these were intensified where Irish Protestants brought with them a militant Orangeism.

Source C: from H. Miller, *Papers relative to the State of Crime in the City of Glasgow* (1840).

In the very centre of the city there is an accumulated mass of squalid wretchedness, which is probably unequalled in any other town in the British dominions. In the dwellings of this area there is concentrated everything that is wretched, evil, loathsome and pestilential. These places are filled by a population of many thousands of miserable creatures. The houses in which they live are unfit even for pigs, and every apartment is filled with a crowd of men, women and children, all in the most revolting state of filth and squalor. In many of the houses there is scarcely any ventilation: dunghills lie in the vicinity of the dwellings; and from the extremely defective sewerage, filth of every kind constantly accumulates. In these horrid dens the most abandoned characters of the city are collected, and from there they nightly issue to spread disease, and to pour upon the town every kind of crime and abomination.

Source D: from a letter on behalf of the Scottish Protestant Churches to the Secretary of State for Scotland, quoted in the *Glasgow Herald*, 25 March 1929.

The process of unregulated migration out of and into Scotland in the past had brought about a situation where there was a danger of the control of the affairs of their own country passing out of the hands of the Scottish people. There is even a danger to the continued existence of Scottish nationality and civilisation. We are convinced that a law-abiding, thrifty and industrious race is being supplanted by immigrants whose presence tends to lower the spirit of independence which has so long been a characteristic of the Scottish people. Scotland is being gradually divided into two great racial camps, different in ideals, with different traditions, and with widely diverging characteristics. These two races do not fuse to any appreciable extent. The tendency is the very reverse. The Irish race in Scotland keep largely by themselves, and their habits are such that our Scottish people do not readily mingle with them.

Source E: from Russel Ward, *The Australian Legend* (1966 edn).

Even among the few Scottish convicts, some rapidly became rich [in Australia]. Among Scottish immigrants, the proportion was undoubtedly much higher. There were probably three main reasons for this. A high proportion of Scottish migrants were middle-class, or tenant farmers. Their Presbyterian faith often came near to equating virtue with material success, but it did instil into their minds the habits of hard work and thrift. And the average standard of education, as much above that of England as England's was above Ireland's, also gave the Scottish migrants an advantage.

[END OF SOURCES FOR SPECIAL TOPIC 6]

SPECIAL TOPIC 6: PATTERNS OF MIGRATION: SCOTLAND 1830s–1930s

Answer *all* of the following questions.

Marks

1. To what extent does the evidence in **Source A** support the views in **Source B** about the effects of Irish immigration on Scottish economic life?

   Compare the content overall and in detail.

   5

2. How accurate a description does **Source C** give of housing conditions experienced by Irish immigrants and Highland migrants in Scottish industrial towns in the 1840s?

   Use the source and recalled knowledge.

   6

3. How fully do **Sources A, B** and **D** explain the reasons for anti-Irish feeling among native Scots?

   *Use **Sources A, B** and **D** and recalled knowledge.*

   8

4. How useful is **Source D** as evidence of how far Irish immigrants had assimilated into Scottish society by the 1930s?

   In reaching a conclusion you should refer to:
   * *the origin and possible purpose of the source;*
   * *the content of the source;*
   * *recalled knowledge.*

   5

5. To what extent does **Source E** reflect the experiences of Scottish emigrants during the nineteenth century?

   Use the source and recalled knowledge.

   6

   (30)

[END OF QUESTIONS ON SPECIAL TOPIC 6]

SPECIAL TOPIC 7: APPEASEMENT AND THE ROAD TO WAR, TO 1939

Study the sources below and then answer the questions which follow.

Source A: cartoon by David Low, *Evening Standard*, 11 March 1936.

"ACH! SO YOU WON'T BE PEACEFUL, HEY? YOU BIG BULLIES!"

Source B: from an article in the *Daily Worker*, the newspaper of the British Communist Party, 12 March 1938.

British people must act. The struggle for British peace and democracy has entered a stage of great tension. In Spain, Franco has launched his offensive. In Austria the great majority of people are heroically fighting for their independence. At the time of writing German troops are massing on the Austrian frontier . . . When are the British people going to pull their weight in this historic struggle? Chamberlain has declared that small nations in Europe need not look to the League of Nations. This is a plain indication to Hitler that so far as Britain is concerned he is free to destroy the independence of Austria and Czechoslovakia.

The British people should be under no illusions. If fascism wins in these countries it will threaten the very existence of democracy in Britain. It is not merely the peace of central Europe that is trembling in the balance. It is the peace of the world.

Source C: from a speech by Lord Londonderry in the House of Lords, 16 March 1938.

It is no good disguising from ourselves that what has happened in Austria was a foregone conclusion. We can see by the enthusiasm with which Hitler is received in Austria that his arrival is welcomed by the great majority of the population.

This change has relieved the terrible tension that has existed in Austria for many years. The great majority of the Austrian population are in favour of the change that has come about. Chancellor Schuschnigg, instead of making a peaceful declaration, has made the situation more dangerous. I think that had the plebiscite taken place it would have been followed by riots, bloodshed and Communist revolution, and we might have seen in Austria the same circumstances as we see in Spain at the present moment. One must feel that the drastic action by Herr Hitler has prevented bloodshed and revolution.

Source D: from Donald Lindsay, *Europe and the World* (1979).

The fall of Austria was the beginning of the end for the Czechs. Their former friends felt that they could do little to save them from being swallowed up in a greater Germany. However, the key to the diplomacy of the next few months lay with the British prime minister, Neville Chamberlain. Hitler had based his hopes on Chamberlain's belief that another war with Germany would be folly and must be avoided at all costs. Every concession that Chamberlain made led Hitler to demand more. Chamberlain's great mistake was not his attempt to remove genuine grievances among the Germans but his belief that Hitler's promises could be trusted.

Source E: from Lord Boothby, *Boothby, Recollections of a Rebel* (1978).

From 1935 until 1939 I watched the political leaders of Britain, in government and in opposition, at pretty close quarters. I reached the conclusion that they were all frightened men. On four occasions Hitler and his gang of bloody murderers could have been brought down, and a second world war averted, by an ultimatum: when he marched into the Rhineland; when he denounced the Treaties of Versailles and Locarno and began to rearm; when he brutally annexed Austria and when (with Chamberlain's support) he attacked Czechoslovakia. Every time we failed to do it. And four times is a lot. The reason for it can, I am afraid, only be put down to a squalid combination of cowardice and greed. The British ministers responsible, instead of being promoted, should have been sacked.

[END OF SOURCES FOR SPECIAL TOPIC 7]

SPECIAL TOPIC 7: APPEASEMENT AND THE ROAD TO WAR, TO 1939

Answer *all* of the following questions.   *Marks*

1. How fully does **Source A** illustrate the problems facing Britain and France as a result of Hitler's remilitarisation of the Rhineland in March 1936?

    Use the source and recalled knowledge.   **6**

2. How valuable is **Source B** as evidence of public opinion at the time of the Anschluss?

    In reaching a conclusion you should refer to:
    *   *the origin and possible purpose of the source;*
    *   *the content of the source;*
    *   *recalled knowledge.*   **5**

3. Compare the views of **Sources B** and **C** concerning the Anschluss in March 1938.

    Compare the content overall and in detail.   **5**

4. How far do you agree with **Source D**'s analysis of Chamberlain's policy during the Czech crisis of September 1938?

    Use the source and recalled knowledge.   **6**

5. How fully do **Sources C, D** and **E** explain the reasons behind British foreign policy in the 1930s?

    *Use **Sources C, D** and **E** and recalled knowledge.*   **8**

                                                                                                (30)

[END OF QUESTIONS ON SPECIAL TOPIC 7]

SPECIAL TOPIC 8: THE ORIGINS AND DEVELOPMENT OF THE COLD WAR 1945–1985

Study the sources below and then answer the questions which follow.

Source A: from a Declaration of the Warsaw Pact Powers, 13 August 1961.

The Western Powers continue to use West Berlin as a centre of subversive activities against the German Democratic Republic (GDR) and all other socialist countries . . . They smuggle their agents into the GDR for all sorts of subversion, recruit spies and incite hostile elements to organize sabotage and provoke disturbances in the GDR.

Due to the aggression of the reactionary forces of the German Federal Republic and its NATO allies, the Warsaw Pact member states must take necessary measures to guarantee their security and, especially, the security of the GDR in the interests of the German people themselves.

The governments of the Warsaw Pact member states propose to establish an order on the borders of West Berlin which will securely block the way to the subversive activity against the socialist countries. In this way reliable safeguards and effective control can be established around the whole territory of West Berlin, including its border with East Berlin.

Source B: from an address by the Mayor of West Berlin, Willy Brandt, before the Berlin Parliament, 13 August 1961.

The measures introduced by the Ulbricht regime at the invitation of the Warsaw Pact States, for sealing off the Soviet zone and the Soviet Sector from West Berlin are a scandalous injustice. They mean that not only a sort of State boundary but the outer wall of a concentration camp is drawn right across Berlin. With the approval of the Eastern Bloc States the Ulbricht regime is making the Berlin situation worse and is overriding yet again legal obligations and the needs of humanity. The Berlin Senate protests against the illegal and inhuman measures taken by the partitioners of Germany, the oppressors of East Berlin and the menacers of West Berlin . . .

By the very admission of the East German authorities, the measures which have just been taken are motivated by the fact that an ever increasing number of inhabitants of East Germany wish to leave this territory. The reasons for this exodus are known. They are simply the internal difficulties in East Germany.

Source C: from S. E. Ambrose and D. G. Brinkley, *Rise to Globalism* (1997).

In August 1962 the Soviet Union began to build medium-range ballistic missile sites in Cuba.

What did Khrushchev hope to accomplish? He could not have expected to achieve a first-strike capability. The American weapons system was far too vast for the Russians to be able to destroy it. Nor could Khrushchev have wanted to expand the arms race, for the Russians would not be able to match American production. Putting missiles in Cuba would not make Castro any more a Communist . . .

The issue in Cuba was prestige . . . The hard-liners in the Soviet Union and the Chinese continued to pressure Khrushchev to stand up to the United States. The Kennedy administration continued to boast about American military superiority. As Theodore Sorensen, Kennedy's chief speech writer, later put it, "These Cuban missiles did not really alter the strategic balance; they only appeared to. But appearances are important in matters of world leadership". The world came close to total destruction over appearances and prestige.

Source D: from the Action Programme of the Czech Communist Party, April 1968.

We must reform the whole political system so that it will permit the dynamic development of socialism and democracy . . .

There must be constitutional freedoms of assembly and association this year to meet . . . the needs of all our people. There should be no bureaucratic interference or monopoly by any individual organization.

The law must also guarantee freedom of speech for minority interests and opinions . . . Freedom of movement, particularly that of travel abroad for our citizens, must be guaranteed by law . . .

The law must protect the personal rights and property of citizens. We must remove laws that put individual citizens at a disadvantage with the state and other institutions.

To make the economy more democratic, we must ensure the independence of businesses from state control and the right to choose jobs freely.

Source E: from *Pravda*, 26 September 1968.

Each Communist party is responsible not only to its own people but also to all the socialist countries and to the entire Communist movement.

The weakening of any link in the world socialist system had a direct effect on all the socialist countries, which could not be indifferent to this. Thus, the antisocialist forces in Czechoslovakia were using talk about the right to self-determination to cover up demands for so-called neutrality and the Czechoslovak Socialist Republic's withdrawal from the socialist alliance. The Communists of the fraternal countries naturally could not remain idle while Czechoslovakia was endangered by antisocialist activity.

[END OF SOURCES FOR SPECIAL TOPIC 8]

SPECIAL TOPIC 8: THE ORIGINS AND DEVELOPMENT OF THE COLD WAR 1945–1985

Answer *all* of the following questions.
Marks

1. How useful is **Source A** in explaining Warsaw Pact concerns over the situation in Berlin in 1961?
   In reaching a conclusion you should refer to:
   • *the origin and possible purpose of the source;*
   • *the content of the source;*
   • *recalled knowledge.* 5

2. Compare the attitudes to the Berlin crisis of 1961 expressed in **Sources A** and **B**.
   Compare the content overall and in detail. 5

3. To what extent does **Source C** provide an adequate explanation for the crisis which developed over Cuba in 1962?
   Use the source and recalled knowledge. 6

4. How far does **Source D** explain the aims of the reform movement in Czechoslovakia in 1968?
   Use the source and recalled knowledge. 6

5. How fully do **Sources B**, **C** and **E** explain the reasons for the tensions between the Superpowers during the 1950s and 1960s?
   *Use **Sources B**, **C** and **E** and recalled knowledge.* 8

   (30)

[END OF QUESTIONS ON SPECIAL TOPIC 8]

SPECIAL TOPIC 9: IRELAND 1900–1985: A DIVIDED IDENTITY

Study the sources below and then answer the questions which follow.

Source A: a Unionist postcard of 1914.

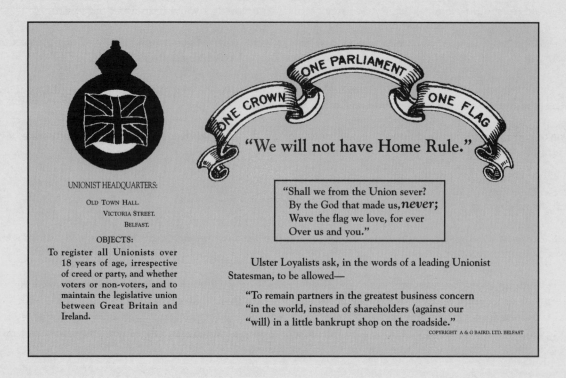

ONE CROWN ONE PARLIAMENT ONE FLAG

"We will not have Home Rule."

UNIONIST HEADQUARTERS:

OLD TOWN HALL.
VICTORIA STREET.
BELFAST.

OBJECTS:

To register all Unionists over 18 years of age, irrespective of creed or party, and whether voters or non-voters, and to maintain the legislative union between Great Britain and Ireland.

"Shall we from the Union sever? By the God that made us, *never*; Wave the flag we love, for ever Over us and you."

Ulster Loyalists ask, in the words of a leading Unionist Statesman, to be allowed—

"To remain partners in the greatest business concern "in the world, instead of shareholders (against our "will) in a little bankrupt shop on the roadside."

COPYRIGHT A & G BAIRD. LTD. BELFAST

Source B: from a speech by John Redmond in the House of Commons, 11 April 1912.

I believe the Home Rule Bill will result in the greater unity and strength of the Empire; I believe it will put an end once and for all to the wretched ill-will, suspicion and disaffection that have existed in Ireland and the suspicion and misunderstanding that have existed between this country and Ireland. I believe it will have the effect of turning Ireland in time . . . into a happy and prosperous country, with a united, loyal, and contented people . . .

Ireland today is peaceful beyond record. She has almost entirely, I believe, cast aside her suspicions and her rancour towards this country. England, on her side, is, I believe today more willing than ever she was in her past history to admit Ireland on terms of equality, liberty, and loyalty, into that great sisterhood of nations that makes up the British Empire.

Source C: from D. M. McCartney, "From Parnell to Pearse", in T. W. Moody and F. X. Martin, *The Course of Irish History*, (1994).

It was not so much the rebellion of Easter week that completed the change in the attitude of the Irish people generally as its aftermath. Of the ninety rebels condemned to death for their part in the insurrection, fifteen, despite a mounting volume of protest, were executed, the first executions being on 3 May and the last ones ending on 12 May. The officials appeared to panic, martial law was imposed, more people were arrested and at least one person shot without trial. The government too, apart from the military, made more mistakes, and the threat of conscription hung over the country. The Irish parliamentary party blundered and lost the initiative. Everything that happened in the next few months played into the hands of Sinn Féin, which made the most of its opportunities.

Source D: from a speech by Arthur Griffith in the Dail Eireann, 19 December 1921.

This is the first Treaty between the representatives of the Irish Government and the representatives of the English Government since 1172 signed on equal footing. It is the first Treaty that admits the equality of Ireland . . . We have brought back the flag; we have brought back the evacuation of Ireland after 700 years by British troops and the formation of an Irish army [applause]. We have brought back to Ireland her full rights and powers of fiscal control. We have brought back to Ireland equality with England, equality with all nations which form that Commonwealth, and an equal voice in the direction of foreign affairs in peace and war.

Source E: from a statement by Eamonn De Valera, September 1922.

If the Republicans stand aside and let the Treaty come into force, it means acceptance of the partition of the country and the abandonment of national sovereignty—a surrender of the ideals for which the sacrifices of the past few years were deliberately made and the suffering of these years consciously endured.

If the Republicans do not stand aside, then they must resist, and resistance means just this. Civil war and armed opposition to what is undoubtedly, as I have said, the decision of the majority of the people.

[END OF SOURCES FOR SPECIAL TOPIC 9]

SPECIAL TOPIC 9: IRELAND 1900–1985: A DIVIDED IDENTITY

Answer *all* of the following questions.   *Marks*

1. How useful is **Source A** as evidence of Unionist opposition to Home Rule?

   In reaching a conclusion you should refer to:
   * *the origin and possible purpose of the source;*
   * *the content of the source;*
   * *recalled knowledge.*   **5**

2. How fully does Redmond in **Source B** illustrate the opinions of the majority of Irish people towards the Home Rule Bill of 1912?

   Use the source and recalled knowledge.   **6**

3. How accurate is **Source C**'s analysis of the impact of the Easter Rising on later political developments in Ireland?

   Use the source and recalled knowledge.   **6**

4. Compare the views expressed in **Sources D** and **E** on Irish attitudes to the Anglo-Irish Treaty.

   Compare the content overall and in detail.   **5**

5. How fully do **Sources A, C** and **E** illustrate the main causes of tension in Ireland between 1912 and 1922?

   *Use **Sources A, C** and **E** and recalled knowledge.*   **8**

                                                                                                       (30)

[END OF QUESTIONS ON SPECIAL TOPIC 9]

[END OF QUESTION PAPER]

[BLANK PAGE]

2004 | Higher

[BLANK PAGE]

X044/301

NATIONAL
QUALIFICATIONS
2004

MONDAY, 31 MAY
9.00 AM – 10.20 AM

HISTORY
HIGHER
Paper 1

Answer questions on **one** Option only.

Take particular care to show clearly the Option chosen. On the **front** of the answer book, **in the top right-hand corner**, write A or B or C.

Within the Option chosen, answer **two** questions, one from Historical Study: Scottish and British and one from Historical Study: European and World.

All questions are assigned 25 marks.

Marks may be deducted for bad spelling and bad punctuation, and for writing that is difficult to read.

SCOTTISH
QUALIFICATIONS
AUTHORITY

[BLANK PAGE]

OPTION A: MEDIEVAL HISTORY

**Answer TWO questions, one from Historical Study: Scottish and British
and one from Historical Study: European and World**

Historical Study: Scottish and British
Medieval Society

1. How far was feudal land-holding the basis of royal power in twelfth-century Scotland and England?

2. Discuss the impact of towns on the economies of twelfth-century Scotland and England.

3. How successfully did the Church, both regular and secular, fulfil its role in twelfth-century Scotland and England?

4. To what extent did David I transform Scottish government and society?

5. Was Henry II "a selfish monarch greedy for land, money and power"?

Historical Study: European and World

EITHER

Nation and King

6. Why was Magna Carta important?

7. To what extent were Angevin weaknesses the main reason for Philip II's success in increasing royal authority in France?

8. "It was not his piety but the wealth of French royal lands which made Louis IX a success." Discuss.

9. Do you agree that Wallace's main contribution to Scotland's success in the Wars of Independence was to take over the leadership of the community of the realm in the absence of the king?

OR

Crisis of Authority

10. "Commercial rivalry in the Channel, French support of the Scots and English involvement with Flanders combined to start the Hundred Years' War." Discuss.

11. How far do you agree that the decline of serfdom in the fourteenth century can be attributed solely to the Black Death?

12. Do you consider that the Peasants' Revolt resulted from a desire to abolish serfdom?

13. To what extent did the Great Schism destroy the unity of Christendom?

[Turn over

OPTION B: EARLY MODERN HISTORY

**Answer TWO questions, one from Historical Study: Scottish and British
and one from Historical Study: European and World**

Historical Study: Scottish and British

EITHER

Scotland in the Age of the Reformation 1542–1603

1. Why did attempts to reform the Church in Scotland before 1560 fail?

2. How far was the progress of the Reformation in Scotland affected by Scotland's relations with England and France?

3. Do you agree that in losing her throne Mary, Queen of Scots, "had nobody to blame but herself"?

4. How effective were the measures taken by James VI to assert his authority throughout Scotland?

5. To what extent did the relationship between Crown and Church change between 1542 and 1603?

OR

Scotland and England in the Century of Revolutions 1603–1702

6. "James I's problems with his English Parliament arose from the fact that he was a 'foreigner'." How far do you agree?

7. To what extent was religion the most significant cause of Charles I's unpopularity in Scotland by 1640?

8. How far do you agree that the Protectorate failed mainly because government relied too heavily on the army?

9. "Neither Glorious nor a Revolution." How accurate is this assessment of the events of 1688–1689 in Scotland and England?

10. To what extent was the Royal Prerogative limited by the struggles between King and Parliament in the seventeenth century?

Historical Study: European and World

EITHER

Royal Authority in 17th and 18th Century Europe

11. "Louis XIV made no significant change in the system of government he inherited." Discuss.

12. Why did Louis XIV order the revocation of the Edict of Nantes in 1685?

13. How far is it true that Frederick the Great's enlightened policies brought no benefit to his subjects?

14. "Joseph II's reforms were more practical than idealistic." How far do you agree?

OR

The French Revolution: The Emergence of the Citizen State

15. Which social groups in France suffered most under the Ancien Régime?

16. Assess the importance of economic issues in causing the outbreak of revolution in 1789.

17. How important a factor was the outbreak of war in 1792 in causing the "Reign of Terror"?

18. To what extent did the French Revolution succeed in creating a new social order in France by 1799?

[Turn over

OPTION C: LATER MODERN HISTORY

**Answer TWO questions, one from Historical Study: Scottish and British
and one from Historical Study: European and World**

Historical Study: Scottish and British

Britain 1850s–1979

1. "Support of the Trade Unions was crucial in the establishment of the Labour Party by 1906." How far would you agree?

2. How effectively did the movements for women's suffrage promote their cause?

3. "The 1930s were years of continuous economic hardship for the people of Britain." How far would you agree?

4. Assess the impact of the welfare reforms of the Labour Government 1945–1951 on the lives of the British people.

5. **Either**

   (a) How much change did urbanisation bring to the lives of the Scottish people between 1880 and 1939?

   Or

   (b) To what extent did Scotland acquire a distinct political identity between 1930 and 1979?

Historical Study: European and World

EITHER

The Growth of Nationalism

6. Why did nationalism grow in **either** Germany **or** Italy between 1815 and 1850?

7. **Either**

    (*a*) Does Bismarck deserve his reputation as the man who united Germany?

    Or

    (*b*) Does Cavour deserve his reputation as the man who united Italy?

8. **Either**

    (*a*) Discuss the view that German foreign policy between 1871 and 1914 created more problems than it solved.

    Or

    (*b*) How successful was Italy's foreign policy between 1871 and 1914?

9. "A total dictatorship". To what extent is this an accurate description of the power of **either** the Nazi state in Germany 1933–1939 **or** the Fascist state in Italy 1922–1939?

OR

The Large Scale State

The USA

10. Why did black Americans face so many social and economic difficulties during the 1920s?

11. To what extent was the economic boom of the 1920s the result of the laissez-faire policies of Republican governments?

12. Assess the impact of the Wall Street Crash on America by 1932.

13. To what extent were the improvements in civil rights for black Americans by 1968 due to the work of the federal government?

Russia

14. Why was it so difficult for opposition movements to challenge the authority of the Tsarist state between 1881 and 1905?

15. To what extent was the survival of the Tsarist state after 1905 due to the work of Stolypin?

16. Assess the importance of military defeat in weakening the Tsarist state by 1917.

17. How significant was Lenin's role in the establishment of the Soviet State?

[END OF QUESTION PAPER]

[BLANK PAGE]

X044/302

NATIONAL
QUALIFICATIONS
2004

MONDAY, 31 MAY
10.40 AM – 12.05 PM

HISTORY
HIGHER
Paper 2

Answer questions on only **one** Special Topic.

Take particular care to show clearly the Special Topic chosen. On the **front** of the answer book, **in the top right-hand corner**, write the number of the Special Topic.

You are expected to use background knowledge appropriately in answering source-based questions.

Marks may be deducted for bad spelling and bad punctuation, and for writing that is difficult to read.

Some sources have been adapted or translated.

SCOTTISH
QUALIFICATIONS
AUTHORITY

[BLANK PAGE]

OPTION A: MEDIEVAL HISTORY

SPECIAL TOPIC 1: NORMAN CONQUEST AND EXPANSION 1050–1153

Study the sources below and then answer the questions which follow.

Source A: from T. Rowley, *The Normans* (2000).

Just as in Italy, here was a situation with splendid possibilities for an ambitious empire builder. After his coronation William began the task of restoring order to those parts of the kingdom that he had conquered. Further pillage was forbidden and the citizens of London were given a charter confirming their privileges. William promised to demand only acceptable ransoms, and offered a pardon to all those Saxons who had not fought beside Harold. In response to this offer thegns from central and northern England came to make their submission at William's headquarters, now based at Barking. Among them, according to the Norman chronicler William of Poitiers, were the earls Edwin and Morcar. Contemporary accounts suggest that William received them cordially and even suggested that Edwin should marry one of his daughters. Restoring order was now William's priority and so began the process of Normanising England. In England, just as in Italy, the Normans were to prove their military and diplomatic skills, and their special genius for adapting existing institutions for their own ends.

Source B: from *The History of the English People* by Henry, Archdeacon of Huntingdon (*c*.1130).

In King William's twenty-first year (1087), when the Normans had fulfilled the just will of the Lord upon the English people, and there was scarcely a noble of English descent in England, but all had been reduced to service of others, and it was even disgraceful to be called English, William, the agent of this vengeance, died. For God had chosen the Normans to wipe out the English nation, because he had seen that the Normans surpassed all other people in their savagery. Indeed, their character is such that when they have brought their enemies so low that they can cast them down no further, they bring themselves down, and reduce their lands to poverty and waste. Always the lords of the Normans, when they have crushed their enemies, since they cannot avoid acting brutally, crush their own men also in wars.

SPECIAL TOPIC 1 continues on *Page five* and fold out *Page six*

Source C: examples of Norman architecture.

Highly ornate south doorway at Rochester Cathedral, Kent. The stonework above the doorway is typical of the Norman decorative sculpture, both in Britain and in Europe.

The elaborately carved doorway at Kilpeck (Hereford and Worcester), dating from the mid twelfth century.

Source D: from R. Welldon Finn, *The Norman Conquest and its effect on the economy* (1971).

Taken at their face value, the figures of Domesday Book show considerable apparent increase in the value of manors over much of England south of the River Trent, even in some shires which Duke William's ruthless invading army had passed through. The figures, more often than not, show us that there was a willingness to rent a property for a sum higher than that of the value set on it. We might so easily say that here is an England which has recovered from the storms of the Conquest and often from the harsh measures imposed upon rebels. On the whole, it is more prosperous than it had been in the more tranquil days of the Confessor and having the potential to develop its economy further.

But from the Englishman's point of view, the Norman Conquest was a catastrophe. Whatever Domesday Book may seem to say, the chroniclers leave us in no doubt as to the immediate effects of the foreign influx. The newcomers, "distressed the wretched folk, and always after that it grew much worse". Invasion, conquest and rebellion inevitably brought in their train the burning of farm buildings and implements and produce, the taking and slaughter of livestock, and a dip in the population. Though all were comparatively readily replaceable, lack of capital and lowered resistance to disease would slow any recovery. Land values dropped and there was a general failure to recover the prosperity of King Edward's day.

SPECIAL TOPIC 1 continues on *Page six*

Source E: from the Charters of Deer (*c.* 1131–1144).

David, the King of Scots, to all his true men, greetings.

Know that the clerics of Deer are quit and immune from all service [required] of laymen, and from unjust taxation; as it has been written in their book; and as they have confirmed at Banff, and have sworn at Aberdeen. Wherefore I strictly command that none shall presume to inflict injury upon them, or their cattle.

[END OF SOURCES FOR SPECIAL TOPIC 1]

SPECIAL TOPIC 1: NORMAN CONQUEST AND EXPANSION 1050–1153

Answer *all* of the following questions.

Marks

1. How far does **Source A** support the view that the process by which Norman influence increased was similar in England and southern Italy?
   Use the source and recalled knowledge. **7**

2. Assess the value of **Source B** as evidence of the treatment of the English people by William.
   In reaching a conclusion you should refer to:
   • *the origin and possible purpose of the source;*
   • *the content of the source;*
   • *recalled knowledge.* **5**

3. Compare the evidence in **Sources B** and **C** about the influence of the Normans on English society.
   Compare the content overall and in detail. **4**

4. Evaluate the impact of William's reign on England.
   *Use **Sources A, C** and **D** and recalled knowledge.* **8**

5. How fully does **Source E** illustrate David I's Normanisation of Scotland?
   Use the source and recalled knowledge. **6**

   (30)

[END OF QUESTIONS ON SPECIAL TOPIC 1]

SPECIAL TOPIC 2 begins on *Page seven*

SPECIAL TOPIC 2: THE CRUSADES 1096–1204

Study the sources below and then answer the questions which follow.

Source A: from reasons given by the Burgundian Stephen I of Neublans for going on Crusade.

Considering how many are my sins and the love, clemency and mercy of Our Lord Jesus Christ; [and] because when Jesus was rich he became poor for our sake, I have determined to repay him in some measure for everything he has given me freely, although I am unworthy. And so I have decided to go to Jerusalem, where God was seen as man and spoke with men, and to adore in the place where his feet trod.

Source B: the siege of Tyre in November 1187, from Ibn al-Athir, *The Sum of World History*, written in the early thirteenth century.

Throughout the whole of his youth, Saladin had never stopped for long to attack a city but had taken them all within a few days without any trouble or difficulty. Thus when he and his advisers saw that Tyre was a problem of a different order they grew bored and decided to leave. The sole responsibility for Tyre's resistance lies with Saladin, who had sent all the Frankish forces rushing off there and reinforced them with men and money from Acre, Ascalon, Jerusalem and elsewhere, for he allowed them all to depart freely and sent them to Tyre. As a result there was there a concentration of Frankish knights from Palestine with their money as well as the wealth of the merchants and the others. All of these defended the city and wrote to the Franks abroad asking their help. This they were promised, and were ordered to hold on to Tyre as a focus of foreign aid and a place of rescue and protection.

SPECIAL TOPIC 2 continues on *Pages eight* and *nine*

Source C: from A. Maalouf, *The Crusades Through Arab Eyes* (1983).

In the eyes of history, Saladin's dislike of needless bloodshed, his strict respect for his commitments, and the touching nobility of his acts of compassion are as valuable as his conquests. Nevertheless, there is no doubt that in 1187 he made a serious political and military error. He knew that by taking Jerusalem he was issuing a challenge to the West, and that the West would respond. In these conditions, to permit thousands of Franks to entrench themselves in Tyre, the most powerful stronghold on the coast, was to offer an ideal beach-head for a fresh invasion. This was especially so since in the absence of King Guy, who was still a captive, the knights had found a particularly determined leader in the man the Arab chroniclers would call al-Markish, the marquis Conrad of Montferrat, who had recently arrived from Europe.

Source D: a map and plan of Richard's advance from Acre to Jaffa in 1191 (1) and a plan of his army at Arsuf. (2)

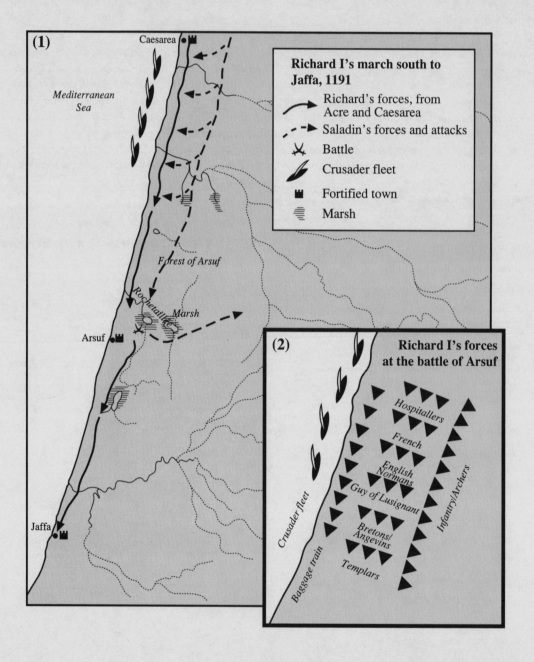

SPECIAL TOPIC 2 continues on *Page nine*

Source E: from Ibn al-Athir, *The Sum of World History*, written in the early thirteenth century.

They used to draw all their supplies from the coast, but when they had moved far inland, the Moslems began attacking their convoys and pillaging them as they went along the road. Then said the king of England to the Franks of Syria who were with them, "Draw me a plan of Jerusalem, for I have never seen it". And they drew him up a plan of the city. And, looking at it, he saw the valley which surrounds the town everywhere except for a small space towards the north. Then he began to question concerning this valley and its depth. And they told him how it was deep and difficult to cross, and then he said,

"It will be impossible to take this town so long as Saladin lives and the Moslems are at peace one with the other. For if we lay siege on this side the other sides will be open, and by them will men and provisions be able to enter. Whereas if we divide our host and siege it on either side Saladin will gather his army and attack one section. Nor will the other party be able to come to help its fellows for fear lest those in the town should make an attack on its camp".

[END OF SOURCES FOR SPECIAL TOPIC 2]

SPECIAL TOPIC 2: THE CRUSADES 1096–1204

Answer *all* of the following questions.

Marks

1. To what extent does **Source A** explain the popularity of the crusading movement in the eleventh century?
   Use the source and recalled knowledge.   6

2. Compare the views of Saladin expressed in **Sources B** and **C**.
   Compare the content overall and in detail.   5

3. How fully do the map and plan in **Source D** explain why Richard I's march from Acre to Jaffa was successful?
   Use the source and recalled knowledge.   6

4. How useful is **Source E** as evidence of the reasons why Richard did not attack Jerusalem?
   In reaching a conclusion you should refer to:
   • *the origin and possible purpose of the source;*
   • *the content of the source;*
   • *recalled knowledge.*   5

5. Was Richard a better leader than Saladin?
   *Use **Sources C**, **D** and **E** and recalled knowledge.*   8

                                                                          (30)

[END OF QUESTIONS ON SPECIAL TOPIC 2]

OPTION B: EARLY MODERN HISTORY

SPECIAL TOPIC 3: SCOTLAND 1689–1715

Study the sources below and then answer the questions which follow.

Source A: from an address by the General Convention of Royal Burghs, 29 October 1706.

By an incorporating Union, our monarchy is suppressed, our Parliaments destroyed. As a result our religion, Church government, Claim of Right, laws, liberties, trade and all that is dear to us is daily in danger of being interfered with, altered or completely undermined by the English. In a British Parliament, the poor representation allowed for Scotland can never secure our interest.

And by these articles our poor people are made liable to the English taxes, which is a certain insupportable burden. The trade proposed is uncertain, and wholly precarious . . . The most considerable branches of our trade differ from those of England, and may be yet more discouraged by their laws.

Source B: from a petition from the Burgh of Montrose in favour of the Union, 15 October 1706.

We are not at all surprised to hear from you that there are some who are not at all pleased with the Union. There were never any good laws of Scotland that were unanimously agreed to . . . These gentlemen who are against the Union do not mention the advantage of the Union.

[Unless there is a Union,] the English will undoubtedly bring back the laws which were repealed last session of Parliament in order to facilitate the treaty. We shall thus be deprived of the only valuable branch of our trade, the only trade of which the balance is on our side. And then one needs not the gift of prophecy to foretell what shall be the fate of this poor miserable nation in a few years.

Source C: from the memoirs of George Lockhart of Carnwath.

Since compiling these memoirs a further discovery has been made, confirming what was suspected. That money was sent to Scotland from England and employed in bribing Members of Parliament.

. . . It was discovered and reported back to the British Parliament by the Commissioners appointed by Parliament that . . . a sum of 20 000 pounds Sterling was sent by the Treasury of England to the Earl of Glasgow in the Year of 1706.

It is abundantly disgraceful for anyone to contribute to the Misery and Ruin of his native country. But if persons of quality and distinction sell, and even at so cheap a price, themselves and their descendants, let their memories be hateful to all future generations.

Source D: from Ian D. Whyte, *Scotland's Society and Economy in Transition c.1500–c.1760* (1997).

There has been considerable debate concerning the motives that prompted Scots commissioners and parliamentarians to support or oppose union. One view has emphasised Scotland's economic crisis as a major factor on the union debate. The other approach has focused on the role of parties and political management in bringing about the union.

Source E: from Bruce Lenman, *The Jacobite Risings in Britain 1689–1746* (1980).

Opponents of the . . . [union] . . . said it was desperately unpopular. Its supporters publicly denied this but in private agreed that it was extremely unpopular, for they were careful not to allow the Scottish constituencies to elect the Scottish representatives to a new parliament. This would only have been inserted into the treaty by men who were frightened of an anti-unionist landslide in an early election. The Jacobites certainly regarded the union as a major political gift to them, for it handed them the leadership of the national sentiment in Scotland.

[END OF SOURCES FOR SPECIAL TOPIC 3]

SPECIAL TOPIC 3: SCOTLAND 1689–1715

Answer *all* of the following questions.

Marks

1. How valuable is **Source A** as evidence of opposition in Scotland to the Treaty of Union?
   In reaching a conclusion you should refer to:
   - *the origin and possible purpose of the source;*
   - *the content of the source;*
   - *recalled knowledge.*
       5

2. Compare the views in **Sources A** and **B** concerning the arguments for and against the Treaty of Union.
   Compare the content overall and in detail.
       5

3. How fully does **Source B** explain the arguments for the Union in 1707?
   Use the source and recalled knowledge.
       6

4. How adequately do **Sources B, C** and **D** explain the motives of the Scottish parliament in accepting the Treaty of Union?
   *Use **Sources B, C** and **D** and recalled knowledge.*
       8

5. To what extent was the Treaty of Union a cause of the Jacobite Rebellion of 1715?
   *Use **Source E** and recalled knowledge.*
       6

    (30)

[END OF QUESTIONS ON SPECIAL TOPIC 3]

SPECIAL TOPIC 4: THE ATLANTIC SLAVE TRADE

Study the sources below and then answer the questions which follow.

Source A: from Peter J. Kitson, *Slavery, Abolition and Emancipation: Volume 2 The Abolition Debate* (1999).

There was surprisingly little criticism of slavery and the slave trade prior to 1780. Few seemed especially concerned about the plight of the African slave. This was largely because Africans suffered from an established prejudice against their skin colour. This made it easier to regard them as inferior to Europeans and therefore suitable for slave labour, believed to be essential to the prosperity of the colonies and the mother country. . . . In addition, it was widely believed that the Africans had been enslaved and sold by other Africans as an alternative to being killed as criminals or prisoners of war, rather than being kidnapped, as was more often the case. Anyway, it was felt that the Africans were savages who would benefit from being removed to a civilised Christian environment.

Source B: from Joseph Woods, *Thoughts on the Slavery of Negroes* (1784).

The objection [to ending slavery and the slave trade] from motives of commercial policy, amounts to this – that the claims of religion and morality ought to be less important than those of greed and luxury, and that [it] is better that thousands of poor unoffending people should be degraded and destroyed than that the inhabitants of Europe should pay a higher price for their rum, rice and sugar . . .

The slave trade is a disgraceful commerce because no right exists to alienate from another his liberty and therefore every purchase of a slave is a contradiction to the original rights of mankind.

Any inquiry into this subject must surely terminate in a call for the total abolition of slavery and, till that be accomplished, for some authoritative act to prohibit the importation of slaves.

Source C: from a speech by Mr Molineux, in a debate in the House of Commons, 1789.

The abolition of the slave trade would destroy the West India Trade. What were they about to do? Did they mean to swallow all the property of the planters in order to show humanity towards the Africans? Before they were humane to these, they should be kind towards their own subjects, whom they had encouraged to risk their property in this trade.

Source D: from Molly Knowles, "Inscription for a Tobacco Box" (1788).

> Though various colours the human face adorn
> To glorious liberty mankind are born
> O, may the hand which raised this favourite weed
> Be loosed in mercy and the slave be freed

Source E: from Samuel Taylor Coleridge, *On the Slave Trade* (1796).

What is the first and constantly acting cause of the slave trade? Is it not self-evidently the consumption of its products? And does not then the guilt rest on the consumers?

If only one tenth part among you who profess yourselves Christians, if one half only of the petitioners were to leave off – not all the West India commodities – but only Sugar and Rum, all this misery might be stopped. . . . A part of your food is sweetened with our brothers' blood. Will God bless the food which is polluted with the blood of his own innocent children?

[END OF SOURCES FOR SPECIAL TOPIC 4]

SPECIAL TOPIC 4: THE ATLANTIC SLAVE TRADE

Answer *all* of the following questions.

Marks

1. How fully does **Source A** explain the reasons for British attitudes towards the slave trade before 1780?
   Use the source and recalled knowledge.   **7**

2. How valuable is **Source B** as evidence of the arguments used by opponents of the slave trade?
   In reaching a conclusion you should refer to:
   • *the origin and possible purpose of the source;*
   • *the content of the source;*
   • *recalled knowledge.*   **5**

3. Compare the views in **Sources B** and **C** on the case for abolishing the slave trade.
   Compare the content overall and in detail.   **5**

4. How fully do **Sources B**, **D** and **E** reflect the methods used by the abolitionists to influence public opinion?
   *Use **Sources B**, **D** and **E** and recalled knowledge.*   **8**

5. To what extent did the prediction made in **Source C** about the likely effects of abolishing the slave trade prove to be accurate?
   Use the source and recalled knowledge.   **5**

(30)

[END OF QUESTIONS ON SPECIAL TOPIC 4]

SPECIAL TOPIC 5: THE AMERICAN REVOLUTION

Study the sources below and then answer the questions which follow.

Source A: from a speech in the House of Commons by Edmund Burke on American Taxation, 19 April 1774.

Whilst England pursued trade, and forgot revenue, you not only acquired commerce, but you actually created the very objects of trade in America. By that creation you raised the trade of England at least four-fold. America had the benefit of your money. She had another benefit, which you are now going to take away from her. She had almost every mark of a free people in all her internal concerns. She had a constitution like that of Britain. She was taxed by her own representatives. She chose most of her own magistrates. She paid them all.

. . . Ask yourselves this question; will America be content in a state of slavery? If not, look to the consequences. Reflect how you are to govern a people, who think they ought to be free, and think they are not. Your scheme yields no revenue; it yields nothing but discontent, disorder, disobedience; and such is the state of America, that after wading up to your eyes in blood you could only end just where you began; that is, to tax where no revenue is to be found.

Source B: from a memorandum by King George III, 1774.

There is no denying the serious crisis to which the disputes between the Mother Country and its North American Colonies are growing, and that the greatest firmness is necessary to bring matters to a good end. Had the Americans in pressing their ill grounded claims put on an appearance of mildness it might have been very difficult to chalk out the right path to be pursued. But they have boldly stated that nothing less than a total independence from the British Parliament will satisfy them. This indeed decides the proper plan to be followed, which is to stop the trade of all those Colonies who obey the order of the Congress for non importation, non exportation, and non consumption.

Source C: from the Olive Branch Petition, 1775.

We support your Majesty's person, family and government, with all devotion that principle and affection can inspire, and are connected with Great Britain by the strongest ties that can unite societies. We deplore every event that tends in any degree to weaken them, we solemnly assure your Majesty that we not only most greatly desire that the former harmony between her and these colonies may be restored, but that an agreement may be established between them on so firm a basis as to preserve its blessings, uninterrupted by any future disagreements . . .

We therefore beg your Majesty that your royal authority and influence may be graciously used to secure for us a happy and permanent reconciliation.

Source D: from a letter from George Washington to Joseph Reed, May 1780.

We ought not to deceive ourselves. The naval resources of Great Britain are more substantial than those of France and Spain united. Her commerce is more extensive than that of both her rivals . . . In modern wars the largest purse must chiefly determine the event. I fear that our enemy will be found to have the largest purse. I have no doubt that ample means will be found to prosecute the war with the greatest vigour.

France is in a very different position. . . . If the war continues for another campaign France will be obliged to impose the taxes usual in time of war which are very heavy, and which the people of France are not in a condition to endure for any duration. When this necessity commences France makes war on ruinous terms; and England will find it much easier to supply her needs.

Source E: from Anne S. K. Brown, "The French Intervention" in J. Williams (ed.), *The American War of Independence 1775–1783* (1974).

The critical point of the campaign began. Aware that a British fleet was sailing to the Chesapeake, de Grasse was anxiously awaiting the arrival of the seven French ships from Newport bringing the siege artillery, when on 5 September 1781, the British fleet of 24 ships of the line was sighted off the Capes. Though 2400 men of his fleet were absent, conveying Saint-Simon's troops ashore, de Grasse promptly went out to meet them and, in the epic battle of the Chesapeake, defeated them and forced them to retire. It was probably in this action, more than in any other, that the independence of the American Colonies was assured.

[*END OF SOURCES FOR SPECIAL TOPIC 5*]

SPECIAL TOPIC 5: THE AMERICAN REVOLUTION

Answer *all* of the following questions.

Marks

1. To what extent does **Source A** explain the reasons for the colonial challenge to British control in America?
   Use the source and recalled knowledge.   **7**

2. Compare the attitudes to the crisis expressed in **Sources B** and **C**.
   Compare the content overall and in detail.   **5**

3. How useful is **Source C** as evidence of the colonists' wishes in 1775?
   In reaching a conclusion you should refer to:
   * *the origin and possible purpose of the source;*
   * *the content of the source;*
   * *recalled knowledge.*   **4**

4. How accurate is Washington's assessment in **Source D** of British advantages in the American War of Independence?
   Use the source and recalled knowledge.   **6**

5. How important was foreign intervention in colonial victory in the war?
   *Use **Sources A**, **D** and **E** and recalled knowledge.*   **8**

   (30)

[*END OF QUESTIONS ON SPECIAL TOPIC 5*]

OPTION C: LATER MODERN HISTORY

SPECIAL TOPIC 6: PATTERNS OF MIGRATION: SCOTLAND 1830s–1930s

Study the sources below and then answer the questions which follow.

Source A: from "Sketches for a portrait of Glasgow" in *Scotland – 1938* (1938).

I was looking out from the window of a coffee-house in Argyle Street about seven o'clock of a Saturday evening. I heard flute music, then I saw a procession. It was a company of Orangemen in full uniform. They passed, an army terrible with banners, and comic, as men that have a good excuse for dressing up. They had just gone by when a new music came to us and a new procession appeared. They were Hibernians, terrible and comic also. "Orangemen and Hibernians!" we said to ourselves, "What will happen if they meet?" Being wise youths we did not follow to see but we met a man later who swore he had witnessed the event. The Hibernians discovered that the Orangemen were in front and so quickened their pace. The Orangemen, hearing also, slowed down. Some resourceful and sporting policemen diverted both parties into a side street and left them to fight it out. Such incidents give Glasgow afternoons and evenings their distinctive flavour!

Source B: from an essay by Professor Tom Devine, *The Herald*, 18 July 1998.

Scotland between 1920 and 1939 was a deeply divided society. This casts some doubt on the view of those scholars who argue optimistically that the absorption of the Catholic Irish and their descendants represent one of the great triumphs of Scottish history. That may be true from the perspective of the 1990s but not from that of earlier decades. The road to integration was long and, at times, a very hard and rocky one. Many of the "Scoto-Irish" who attracted such intense racial abuse from elements within the host community had been living in Scotland for three generations yet were still labelled as alien "Irish". In the nineteenth century sectarianism was then confined to job discrimination, Orange walks and occasional disturbances. The Irish in Scotland may not have been liked but for the most part were regarded with indifference. Dundee and Edinburgh were quiet and even in Glasgow sectarian violence was much less than in Liverpool. Scottish Catholics had earned generous praise for their contribution to the Great War and six soldiers from the community had won the Victoria Cross. This context makes the events of the 1920s more difficult to explain.

Source C: from evidence given by Bishop Andrew Scott of Glasgow, in "Report of the Irish Poor in Great Britain" (1836).

I have to remark that, till such time as means can be provided for the education of the children of the poor Roman Catholic Irish immigrants, it will be impossible to make good men, good citizens or good subjects of the rising population of that faith in this country. The parents are so wasteful in their habits that they are unable to pay for their children's education and many do not set a proper value on the benefits of education to their children. There are many charitable schools in Glasgow but the teachers, being all Protestants, always mix up the elements of education with the principles of the Protestant religion. This necessarily excludes Roman Catholic children from attending these schools. An attempt has been made to get schools for the education of these poor people but that attempt, for want of funds, will render it impossible to keep up the schools for themselves.

Source D: from M. Lynch, *Scotland: A New History* (1991).

Emigration is a revealing commentary on many aspects of the condition of the Scottish working classes in the nineteenth century. Like the early emigrants from the Highlands, there were skilled craftsmen from the Lowlands who took ship, usually to Canada or the USA, in search of better prospects, and their experience is testimony to the extraordinary attraction which the Empire held for the Victorian working-class as much as to conditions at home. Emigrants from the north-east were likely to be small farmers or farm servants, pushed by the harsh pressures of the soil, climate and landlordism and pulled by land-hunger. Their destination was usually Canada, where land was still cheap and plentiful. Other cases underline the remarkable mobility of some sections of the working classes. There were many routes to the emigration ships and the experiences of the Highlanders cleared off their land were not the most common ones.

Source E: from a poem "Manitoba" by John Maclean, 1878.

> I can see nothing now but sheep on the hillsides:
> There is no one left in the glen but a stranger or two:
> The few of them who are left are on headlands by the sea
> Driven to the shore and burdened with rents.
>
> The land-owning proprietors at this time are all too eager
> To grab for themselves the worldly possessions of all the rest;
> Cunning schemes are always being used in the land of Gaels
> To drive the people out and make room for sheep.
>
> The wearers of the kilt and the hose and cocked bonnet,
> Who were always renowned in the forefront of battle
> Are today being driven abroad to unwholesome countries
> With no other purpose but to lay waste the land.

[END OF SOURCES FOR SPECIAL TOPIC 6]

SPECIAL TOPIC 6: PATTERNS OF MIGRATION: SCOTLAND 1830s–1930s

Answer *all* of the following questions.

Marks

1. How useful is **Source A** as evidence of the impact of Irish immigration on law and order in Scottish towns and cities?
   In reaching a conclusion you should refer to:
   * *the origin and possible purpose of the source;*
   * *the content of the source;*
   * *recalled knowledge.*

   4

2. To what extent do you accept the views expressed in **Source B** regarding the effects of Irish immigration on Scottish society by 1939?
   Use the source and recalled knowledge.

   6

3. How fully do **Sources A, B** and **C** illustrate the difficulties faced by Irish immigrants in Scotland between 1830 and 1939?
   *Use **Sources A, B** and **C** and recalled knowledge.*

   8

4. How far does the evidence in **Source E** support the views in **Source D** regarding the reasons for emigration from Scotland during this period?
   Compare the content overall and in detail.

   6

5. To what extent were emigrants from Scotland successful in fulfilling their hopes as identified in **Source D**?
   Use the source and recalled knowledge.

   6

   (30)

[END OF QUESTIONS ON SPECIAL TOPIC 6]

SPECIAL TOPIC 7: APPEASEMENT AND THE ROAD TO WAR, TO 1939

Study the sources below and then answer the questions which follow.

Source A: from a policy memorandum by the Foreign Secretary, Anthony Eden, 8 March 1936.

We must discourage any military action by France against Germany. A possible course would be for the other nations who signed the Locarno treaty to call upon Germany to evacuate the Rhineland. It is difficult now to suppose that Herr Hitler could agree to such a demand, and it certainly should not be made unless the Powers, who made it, were prepared to enforce it by military action. Fortunately, M. Flandin [the French Foreign Minister] has said that France will not act alone but will take the matter to the Council of the League of Nations.

While we obviously cannot object to the Council deciding that Germany has violated the demilitarised zone, this ought not to be followed by a French attack on Germany and a request for our armed assistance. It is in our interest to conclude with Germany as far-reaching and enduring a settlement as possible whilst Herr Hitler is still in the mood to do so.

Source B: from a letter to the editor, *Glasgow Herald*, 16 March 1938.

Many of your correspondents would like Britain to take a more active part on the side of the anarchists, communists and others who make up the so-called government of Spain. There is in fact an international brigade fighting on the government side and the deaths of a few Scots have been reported. These Scots appear to have been of a communist turn of mind and connected with extreme views when in Scotland. It is of course common knowledge that Russia has been deeply interested in Spanish politics for some time. The real point to consider is the fact that in Franco's territory business and social life is going on as normally as difficult conditions permit. When Franco and the Nationalists got control the country settled down at once. There are many in this country who hope that Franco will win and a reign of law and order will return to Spain.

Source C: from a letter to the editor, *Glasgow Herald*, 17 March 1938.

It cannot be repeated too often that, if General Franco and his allies were to win, France would be encircled by hostile states and in the near future we should be faced with a general European war with the Mediterranean closed to us. The policy of a government representing the real interests of the people of Britain should be a return to the League of Nations and to restore to the Spanish government its legal right to purchase arms freely. This step, if taken at the beginning, might have enabled the Spanish government to put down the rebellion. The alternative is to continue giving way to dictators in the name of peace until finally we are left to face them alone. Let us put collective security into practice and save Spain and our democracy before it is too late.

SPECIAL TOPIC 7 continues on *Page nineteen* and fold out *Page twenty*

Source D: a cartoon from *The News of the World*, 25 September 1938.

Source E: from Peijian Shen, *The Age of Appeasement: the Evolution of British Foreign Policy in the 1930s* (1999).

What kind of peace were the appeasers looking for? Their peace did not include Abyssinians, because they rewarded Mussolini with the Hoare-Laval Pact to allow him to launch war on that country . . . their peace was peace "in Europe", perhaps worse than that, because "Europe" here referred only to Western Europe. As to the countries in Central and Eastern Europe, they were, in Chamberlain's eyes, the "faraway nations", although Chamberlain never felt they were too far away to sell them to Hitler. Therefore, the appeasers' hopes were, at best, an illusion of peace in Western Europe, which could be bought at the price of sacrificing peace in the rest of the world.

SPECIAL TOPIC 7 continues on Page twenty

[END OF SOURCES FOR SPECIAL TOPIC 7]

SPECIAL TOPIC 7: APPEASEMENT AND THE ROAD TO WAR, TO 1939

Answer *all* of the following questions.

Marks

1. How fully does **Source A** show the British government's attitude to the remilitarisation of the Rhineland in March 1936?
    Use the source and recalled knowledge.

    6

2. How useful is **Source B** in explaining the issues that led to the British policy of non-intervention in the Spanish Civil War?
    In reaching a conclusion you should refer to:
    *   *the origin and possible purpose of the source;*
    *   *the content of the source;*
    *   *recalled knowledge.*

    5

3. Compare the views of **Sources B** and **C** about the desirability of a Nationalist victory in the Spanish Civil War.
    Compare the content overall and in detail.

    5

4. To what extent does the cartoon (**Source D**) illustrate Chamberlain's policy during the Czech crisis of 1938?
    Use the source and recalled knowledge.

    6

5. How far do **Sources A**, **B** and **E** explain why Britain adopted a policy of appeasement in the 1930s?
    *Use **Sources A**, **B** and **E** and recalled knowledge.*

    8

    (30)

[END OF QUESTIONS ON SPECIAL TOPIC 7]

SPECIAL TOPIC 8 begins on *Page twenty-one*

SPECIAL TOPIC 8: THE ORIGINS AND DEVELOPMENT OF THE COLD WAR 1945–1985

Study the sources below and then answer the questions which follow.

Source A: from Sixteen demands of students at Budapest's Technological University displayed throughout Budapest, 23 October 1956.

3. A new Government must be constituted under the direction of Comrade Imre Nagy; all the criminal leaders of the Stalin-Rakosi era must be immediately relieved of their duties.

4. We demand that . . . Matyas Rakosi, who is the person most responsible for all the crimes of the recent past, as well as for the ruin of our country, must be brought back to Hungary for trial before a people's tribunal.

5. We demand that general elections, by universal, secret ballot, be held throughout the country to elect a new National Assembly, with all political parties participating. We demand that the right of the workers to strike be recognised.

Source B: from A. Gromyko, *Memories* (1989).

I must emphasise as strongly as I can that the help given to Hungary by the Soviet Union was absolutely justified. The forces that were bent on overthrowing the Hungarian leadership intended to destroy the social order and restore the previous system . . .

The internal forces that were hostile to the new post-war Hungary derived help from outside the country. This much was plain from the moment they decided to resort to the use of force and to drown in blood everything that had been achieved in the country liberated by the Soviet army. The foreign circles that condemned the Soviet action have presented the facts in a distorted light. They have generally pretended not to be aware that the Soviet Union was acting in response to numerous and insistent requests from Hungary, from democratic bodies, including that part of the leadership that patriotically stood for the defence of Hungary's social order. As a result, Hungary has remained an independent state among the socialist countries, dedicated to the cause of peace and friendship between the peoples.

In evaluating the events of 1956, the Soviet Union and the people of Hungary have a clear conscience.

SPECIAL TOPIC 8 continues on *Pages twenty-two* and *twenty-three*

Source C: from A. Dobson and S. Marsh, *US Foreign Policy since 1945* (2001).

The Kennedy administration oversaw a major change in the nature of the Cold War and a turning point in containment policy. The development of Mutual Assured Destruction (MAD) shifted the emphasis from outright victory to that of managing an enduring balance between East and West. The new "logic" of the Cold War was for a peaceful resolution and this, for US policy-makers, signalled the end of the drive for victory through military strength. MAD, as the Cuban missile crisis demonstrated in 1962, generated unacceptable levels of brinkmanship. Instead, the emphasis was on collaboration with the Kremlin to assure system stability. Core US–Soviet relations had to be kept in mutually accepted balance at the same time that their intense competition was fought out on the edges of the Cold War, such as in Vietnam.

Although it was never explicitly explained to the American people, containment policy became less about winning, and more about not losing the Cold War.

Source D: from a Memorandum by Undersecretary of State George Ball to President Johnson, 1 July 1965.

The South Vietnamese are losing the war to the Viet Cong. No one can assure you that we can beat the Viet Cong or even force them to the conference table on our terms, no matter how many hundred thousand (US) troops we deploy . . .

The Question to Decide: Should we limit our liabilities in South Vietnam and try to find a way out with minimal long-term costs?

The alternative, no matter what we may wish it to be, is almost certainly a long war involving an open-ended commitment of US forces, mounting US casualties, no assurance of a satisfactory solution, and a serious danger of escalation at the end of the road . . .

The decision you face now, therefore, is crucial. Once large numbers of US troops are committed to direct combat, they will begin to take heavy casualties in a war they are ill-equipped to fight in a non-cooperative if not downright hostile countryside.

Once we suffer large casualties, we will have started an irreversible process. Our involvement will be so great that we cannot, without national humiliation, stop short of achieving our complete objectives. Of the two possibilities I think humiliation would be more likely than the achievement of our objectives – even after we have paid terrible costs.

SPECIAL TOPIC 8 continues on *Page twenty-three*

Source E: from a Memorandum by Secretary of Defence Robert McNamara, 20 July 1965.

We must choose among three courses of action with respect to Vietnam:

(a) Cut our losses and withdraw under the best conditions that can be arranged . . .

(b) Continue at about the present level, with the US forces limited to say 75,000 . . .

(c) Expand the US military pressure against the Viet Cong in the South and maintain the military pressure against the North Vietnamese in the North. At the same time we should launch a political campaign to make clear and communicate our objectives. This alternative would stave off defeat in the short run and offer a good chance of producing a favourable settlement in the longer run. It would imply a commitment to see a fighting war clear through at considerable cost in casualties and material and would make any later decision to withdraw even more difficult and even more costly than would be the case today.

My recommendations are based on the choice of the third alternative.

[END OF SOURCES FOR SPECIAL TOPIC 8]

SPECIAL TOPIC 8: THE ORIGINS AND DEVELOPMENT OF THE COLD WAR 1945–1985

Answer *all* of the following questions.

Marks

1. How useful is **Source A** as evidence of the growth of demand for reform in Hungary in 1956?
   In reaching a conclusion you should refer to:
   * *the origin and possible purpose of the source;*
   * *the content of the source;*
   * *recalled knowledge.*

   5

2. To what extent do you accept Gromyko's defence (**Source B**) of Soviet intervention in Hungary in 1956?
   Use the source and recalled knowledge.

   6

3. How far do you agree with the views in **Source C** on the changing character of the Cold War from the early 1960s onwards?
   Use the source and recalled knowledge.

   6

4. Compare the views expressed in **Sources D** and **E** on American involvement in the Vietnam War.
   Compare the content overall and in detail.

   5

5. How important was ideology in the development of international tension during the Cold War?
   *Use **Sources B, C** and **E** and recalled knowledge.*

   8

   (30)

[END OF QUESTIONS ON SPECIAL TOPIC 8]

SPECIAL TOPIC 9: IRELAND 1900–1985: A DIVIDED IDENTITY

Study the sources below and then answer the questions which follow.

Source A: from Police Intelligence reports from County Cavan, 1914.

All classes displayed a strong patriotic and anti-German feeling, and joined irrespective of creed and politics in giving a hearty send-off to reservists and recruits when leaving to join the army. Nevertheless considerable unrest prevailed in both the unionist and nationalist ranks as to the action the government would take with regard to the Home Rule Bill . . .

The present war is popular with all classes save a few Sinn Féiners, and there is not the slightest sympathy with the Germans; all sections are working cordially together to raise funds for the assistance of dependants of soldiers and sailors involved in the war.

Source B: from a letter by Roger Casement, *Irish Independent*, 17 September 1914.

Ireland has no blood to give to any land to any cause but that of Ireland. Our duty as a Christian people is to abstain from bloodshed; and our duty as Irishmen is to give our lives for Ireland. Ireland needs all her sons . . . The Home Rule Bill is being offered on terms that only a fool would accept. But, even if the Bill were all that is claimed for it, and if it were freely given today, it would still be the duty of Irishmen to save their strength and manhood for the trying tasks before them.

Source C: from J. Smith, *Britain and Ireland: From Home Rule to Independence* (2000).

For all the advance made by Sinn Féin during 1917 and early 1918, its political impact would have remained marginal if not for the British decision to extend conscription to Ireland on 9 April 1918 . . . Irish reaction was uniformly hostile, and Sinn Féin exploited this. Drawing on its current popularity and growing local organisation, it launched a campaign of mass resistance that drew in the wider nationalist community . . .

The campaign against conscription met with a predictable response from the British. Lord French, the new Lord Lieutenant ... used the cover of a "German Plot" to arrest the Sinn Féin leadership. He followed this up with the internment of "suspects" and banning any group connected with the party . . . With much of its political leadership in prison, control of the movement passed to Collins and Mulcahy, who had evaded arrest. Thanks to heavy-handedness from Dublin Castle, the struggle for Irish independence lay firmly with men dedicated to active military resistance to British rule.

Source D: from a speech to his constables by Lt. Col. Smyth, Division Commander for Munster of the Royal Irish Constabulary, 17 June 1920.

If a police barracks is burned or if the barracks already occupied is not suitable, then the best house in the locality is to be commandeered, the occupants thrown into the gutter. Let them die there – the more the merrier. Police and military will patrol the country at least five nights a week. They are not to confine themselves to the main roads, but make across the country, lie in ambush and, when civilians are seen approaching, shout "Hands up!" Should the order be not immediately obeyed, shoot and shoot with effect. If the persons approaching carry their hands in their pockets, or are in any way suspicious-looking, shoot them down. You may make mistakes occasionally and innocent persons may be shot, but that cannot be helped, and you are bound to get the right parties some time. The more you shoot, the better I will like you, and I assure you no policeman will get into trouble for shooting any man.

Source E: from a letter from Lloyd George to the bishop of Chelmsford, 9 April 1921.

I will not attempt to deny that there have been deplorable excesses by the R.I.C. [Royal Irish Constabulary]. Individuals working under conditions of extraordinary personal danger and strain, where they are in uniforms and their adversaries mingle unrecognisable among the ordinary civilian population, have undoubtedly been guilty of unjustifiable acts. A certain number of undesirables have got into the corps, and in the earlier days discipline in the new and difficult conditions took some time to establish . . .

There is no question that, despite all difficulties, discipline is improving, the force is consolidating, and that the acts of indiscipline, despite ambushes, assassinations and outrages, often designed to provoke retaliation for the purposes of propaganda, are becoming increasingly infrequent. When the history of the past nine months in Ireland comes to be written, and the authentic acts of misconduct can be disentangled from the vastly greater mass of lying accusations, the general record of patience displayed by the sorely tried police, by the Auxiliaries as well as by the ordinary Constabulary, will command not condemnation but admiration.

[END OF SOURCES FOR SPECIAL TOPIC 9]

SPECIAL TOPIC 9: IRELAND 1900–1985: A DIVIDED IDENTITY

Answer *all* of the following questions.

Marks

1. How useful is **Source A** as evidence of Irish attitudes towards participation in the First World War?
   In reaching a conclusion you should refer to:
   * *the origin and possible purpose of the source;*
   * *the content of the source;*
   * *recalled knowledge.* **5**

2. To what extent were the opinions expressed in **Source B** influenced by developments in Ireland before 1912?
   Use the source and recalled knowledge. **6**

3. How fully does **Source C** explain the reasons for the growth in support for Sinn Féin in 1917–1918?
   Use the source and recalled knowledge. **6**

4. Compare the views expressed in **Sources D** and **E** on the conduct of the Royal Irish Constabulary during the Anglo-Irish War.
   Compare the content overall and in detail. **5**

5. Why did it prove so difficult to reach an agreement on how Ireland should be governed during the period 1914–1921?
   *Use **Sources B**, **C** and **D** and recalled knowledge.* **8**

   (30)

[END OF QUESTIONS ON SPECIAL TOPIC 9]

[END OF QUESTION PAPER]

[BLANK PAGE]

2005 | Higher

[BLANK PAGE]

X044/301

NATIONAL
QUALIFICATIONS
2005

MONDAY, 23 MAY
9.00 AM – 10.20 AM

HISTORY
HIGHER
Paper 1

Answer questions on **one** Option only.

Take particular care to show clearly the Option chosen. On the **front** of the answer book, **in the top right-hand corner**, write A or B or C.

Within the Option chosen, answer **two** questions, one from Historical Study: Scottish and British and one from Historical Study: European and World.

All questions are assigned 25 marks.

Marks may be deducted for bad spelling and bad punctuation, and for writing that is difficult to read.

SCOTTISH
QUALIFICATIONS
AUTHORITY

[BLANK PAGE]

OPTION A: MEDIEVAL HISTORY

Answer TWO questions, one from Historical Study: Scottish and British and one from Historical Study: European and World

Historical Study: Scottish and British

Medieval Society

1. To what extent was knight service the main characteristic of twelfth-century feudalism?

2. How far do you agree that the secular Church was more important to ordinary people than the regular Church?

3. "The influence of monarchs was the most important reason for the growth of towns in the twelfth century." Discuss.

4. To what extent was David I successful in establishing his authority over Scotland?

5. How far can it be argued that Henry II reformed the justice system in England to strengthen the power of the crown at the expense of the barons?

Historical Study: European and World

EITHER

Nation and King

6. How accurate is it to describe King John of England as a victim of circumstances?

7. Do you agree that Philip II's success can mainly be attributed to his belief that he should be "no man's vassal"?

8. To what extent was Louis IX responsible for the creation of a united French kingdom?

9. "The Scots could not have won the Wars of Independence without Robert Bruce." Discuss.

OR

Crisis of Authority

10. To what extent was French weakness the main reason for English success in the Hundred Years' War up to 1421?

11. How significant an impact did the Hundred Years' War have on France and England?

12. Assess the impact of the Black Death on England, Scotland and continental Europe.

13. How far was the Avignon Papacy responsible for the problems which faced the Church in the fourteenth and fifteenth centuries?

[Turn over

OPTION B: EARLY MODERN HISTORY

**Answer TWO questions, one from Historical Study: Scottish and British
and one from Historical Study: European and World**

Historical Study: Scottish and British

EITHER

Scotland in the Age of the Reformation 1542–1603

1. To what extent did the "rough wooing" force the Scots to adopt a pro-French policy by 1548?

2. Explain the success of the Protestant Reformation in 1560.

3. "Mary ultimately lost the throne not because of her loyalty to Rome but because she entered into a scandalous marriage." How far do you agree?

4. How successful was James VI as king of Scotland before 1603?

5. To what extent was the Reformation of 1560 a significant turning point in Scottish history?

OR

Scotland and England in the Century of Revolutions 1603–1702

6. How far would you agree that the Union of Crowns brought no real advantages to Scotland?

7. Explain the rise of the Covenanter movement in Scotland.

8. "Charles I's obsession with authority and control was the main cause of the English Civil War." Do you agree?

9. Do you agree that the Protectorate offered no more than "a return to old forms of government under new management"?

10. To what extent did the Glorious Revolution settle the issues in the struggles between King and Parliament in the seventeenth century?

Historical Study: European and World

EITHER

Royal Authority in 17th and 18th Century Europe

11. How important was the nobility to the absolute government of Louis XIV?

12. "Of all Louis XIV's domestic policies, it was in religion that he had the least success." How far do you agree?

13. How successful was Frederick II of Prussia as an Enlightened Despot?

14. "Joseph II did little to solve the real problems of the Austrian people." Do you agree?

OR

The French Revolution: The Emergence of the Citizen State

15. How far do you agree that economic problems were the main threat to the stability of the Ancien Régime?

16. Why did the events of 1787–1789 result in revolution?

17. How far was Louis XVI responsible for his own execution?

18. To what extent did France become impossible to govern in the 1790s?

[Turn over

OPTION C: LATER MODERN HISTORY

Answer TWO questions, one from Historical Study: Scottish and British and one from Historical Study: European and World

Historical Study: Scottish and British

Britain 1850s–1979

1. Explain why Parliament gave the right to vote to increasing numbers of people between 1867 and 1928.

2. How far were the reports on poverty produced by Booth and Rowntree responsible for the Liberal social reforms of 1906–1914?

3. To what extent would you agree that the importance of the Suffragettes in gaining votes for women has been exaggerated?

4. How serious an impact did the Great Depression of the 1930s have on Britain?

5. How successful were the social reforms introduced by the Labour Government of 1945–1951?

Historical Study: European and World

EITHER

The Growth of Nationalism

6. How effectively did nationalists promote their cause in **either** Germany **or** Italy between 1815 and 1850?

7. **Either**

   (a) How important was the Zollverein in the achievement of national unification in Germany?

   Or

   (b) Evaluate the contribution of Garibaldi to national unification in Italy.

8. "Between 1871 and 1914 the new nation state attracted little popular support." How far would you agree with reference to **either** Germany **or** Italy during this period?

9. **Either**

   (a) To what extent were economic crises responsible for allowing the Nazis to achieve power in Germany in 1933?

   Or

   (b) "The breakdown of effective parliamentary government in Italy was the major factor in the Fascist rise to power." Discuss.

OR

The Large Scale State

The USA

10. Why did hostility towards immigration become a more serious issue in the USA after 1918?

11. "The business of America is business" (President Coolidge). How accurately does this describe the economic policies of Republican governments during the 1920s?

12. To what extent was the recovery of the USA from the Depression of the 1930s due to the New Deal?

13. To what extent was the growth of black radical movements in the 1960s due to the social and economic problems faced by black Americans in the cities of the North and West?

Russia

14. "Their threats to Tsarism were ineffective and disorganised." Discuss this view of the revolutionary movements in the years up to 1905.

15. "A direct result of Tsarist incompetence and blundering." How far do you agree with this view of the outbreak of the 1905 revolution?

16. Explain why the Provisional Government lost control of Russia in 1917.

17. To what extent was the Bolshevik victory in the Civil War due to Trotsky's skills as a military leader?

[END OF QUESTION PAPER]

[BLANK PAGE]

X044/302

NATIONAL
QUALIFICATIONS
2005

MONDAY, 23 MAY
10.40 AM – 12.05 PM

HISTORY
HIGHER
Paper 2

Answer questions on only **one** Special Topic.

Take particular care to show clearly the Special Topic chosen. On the **front** of the answer book, **in the top right-hand corner**, write the number of the Special Topic.

You are expected to use background knowledge appropriately in answering source-based questions.

Marks may be deducted for bad spelling and bad punctuation, and for writing that is difficult to read.

Some sources have been adapted or translated.

SCOTTISH
QUALIFICATIONS
AUTHORITY

[BLANK PAGE]

OPTION A: MEDIEVAL HISTORY

SPECIAL TOPIC 1: NORMAN CONQUEST AND EXPANSION 1050–1153

Study the sources below and then answer the questions which follow.

Source A: from G. O. Sayles, *The Medieval Foundations of England* (1966).

In the eyes of the English the successor to the throne was obvious, for at home Harold's claims were quite undisputed. He was the brother-in-law of the late king and, though this was not a blood relationship with the royal house of Wessex, yet the royal blood of the Danish dynasty ran in his veins. Furthermore, there is really good authority for his assertion that Edward had on his death bed named him as his heir. The wishes of a reigning monarch had much to do in deciding a successor . . . And for twelve years Harold had been the real protector and ruler of the kingdom and had proved his strength of character, his abilities as a statesman and his appreciation of the true line of English traditions . . .

William had little he could say on his own behalf. He was a cousin of the Confessor, but this relationship arose from marriage connections only and this had never been used in England as the basis of a claim to kingship.

William stressed the fact that in 1064 Harold had bound himself to him by an oath when the accident of a shipwreck had placed him in the hands of the Norman duke. What kind of oath it was we do not know: English writers say nothing about it, Norman writers say too much and most of it contradictory.

Source B: from M. Chibnall, *The Debate on the Norman Conquest* (1999).

When King Edward the Confessor died childless on 5 January 1066, he left no clear successor, and there were any number of possible claimants . . . The two strongest contenders were the man on the spot, Harold Godwinson, earl of Wessex, and William, duke of Normandy. Harold could offer no more than an extremely dubious claim to kinship; but he was the wealthiest and most powerful of the earls and the brother of King Edward's wife Edith . . .

When Cnut's direct line died out in 1042, Edward returned to England with some Norman backing, and it was widely believed in Normandy that he had named Duke William as his heir. So contradictory claims existed in England and Normandy before 1066.

The Normans increased their claim in 1064, when Harold Godwinson, on a mission to Normandy . . . was shipwrecked off the coast of Ponthieu, taken prisoner by Count Guy, and released only through the intervention of Duke William. The Normans alleged that he had voluntarily become William's vassal and had taken a solemn oath on relics to further his succession.

Source C: from the *Ecclesiastical History* of Orderic Vitalis, written *c.* 1114–1141.

Then Earl Copsi, the sons of Aethelgar, grandsons of King Edward, and many other men of wealth and high birth made their peace with William, and were allowed to keep all their possessions honourably when they had sworn fealty. The king went on from there to other parts of his kingdom, and everywhere arranged affairs to the advantage of the inhabitants as well as of himself. He appointed strong men from his Norman forces as guardians of the castles, and distributed rich fiefs that induced men to endure toil and danger to defend them.

Source D: from the *Ecclesiastical History* of Orderic Vitalis, written *c.* 1114–1141.

King William was justly renowned for his reforming zeal. In particular he loved true religion in churchmen for on this the peace and prosperity of the world depend . . . For when a bishop or abbot had come to the end of his life and died . . . the wise king appointed as bishop or abbot whoever seemed to his highest counsellors specially distinguished in life and doctrine. He followed this course for the fifty-six years that he ruled the duchy of Normandy and kingdom of England, so leaving a pious precedent for others to follow. Simony* was detestable to him, and so in appointing abbots or bishops he gave less weight to wealth and power than to wisdom and a good life. He appointed abbots of known virtue to the English monasteries, so that by their zeal and discipline monasticism, which had for a time been lax and faltering, revived and was restored to its former strength.

* Simony — paying money to be appointed to a church post.

Source E: from the speech of Robert Bruce (I) to David I at the Battle of the Standard, from *The Standard*, written by Ailred, abbot of Rievaulx in Yorkshire, in the mid twelfth century.

Against whom do you bear arms today and lead this huge army? Against the English, truly, and the Normans. O king, these are the men who have always given you useful counsel and ready help, and willing obedience besides.

Now you seek to destroy those through whom the kingdom was obtained for you. Who but our army restored Edgar, your brother, to the kingdom? You yourself, O king, when you demanded from your brother Alexander the part of the kingdom which Edgar had left to you at his death, obtained it without bloodshed through the fear of us.

[END OF SOURCES FOR SPECIAL TOPIC 1]

SPECIAL TOPIC 1: NORMAN CONQUEST AND EXPANSION 1050–1153

Answer *all* of the following questions.

Marks

1. Compare the views of Sayles (**Source A**) and Chibnall (**Source B**) about the rival claimants to the throne in 1066.
   Compare the sources overall and in detail.

   4

2. How fully does **Source C** explain the ways in which William established his control in England?
   Use the source and recalled knowledge.

   6

3. Is there sufficient evidence in **Source D** to argue that William reformed the Church in England?
   Use the source and recalled knowledge.

   7

4. How reliable is **Source E** as an explanation of why David I brought Anglo-Norman barons to Scotland?
   In reaching a conclusion you should refer to:
   * *the origin and possible purpose of the source;*
   * *the content of the source;*
   * *recalled knowledge.*

   5

5. To what extent was there a Norman achievement in Europe?
   *Use **Sources C, D** and **E** and recalled knowledge.*

   8

   (30)

[END OF QUESTIONS ON SPECIAL TOPIC 1]

SPECIAL TOPIC 2: THE CRUSADES 1096–1204

Study the sources below and then answer the questions which follow.

Source A: from a history of the First Crusade by the German monk Ekkehard, written *c.* 1101.

After Urban had aroused the spirits of all by the promise of forgiveness to those who undertook the crusade with single-hearted devotion, almost one hundred thousand men were appointed to the immediate service of God. They came from Aquitaine and Normandy, England, Scotland, Ireland, Brittany, Galicia, Gascony, France, Flanders, Lorraine, and from other Christian peoples, whose names I no longer retain. It was truly an army of "crusaders", for they bore the sign of the cross on their garments as a reminder that they should mortify the flesh, and in the hope that they would in this way triumph over the enemies of the cross of Christ. Thus, through the marvellous working of God's will, all these members of Christ, so different in speech, origin and nationality, were suddenly brought together as one body through their love of Christ.

Source B: from the *History of the Franks who captured Jerusalem*, by Raymond d'Aguilers, written in 1101.

And so, as we said, when our men were in a panic and while they were on the verge of despair, divine mercy was at hand for them . . . Thus, when the city of Antioch had been captured, the Lord, employing His power and kindness, chose a certain poor peasant through whom He comforted us . . . On that day, after the necessary preparations, and after every one had been sent out of the Church of St. Peter, twelve men, together with that man who had spoken of the Lance, began to dig . . . And after we had dug from morning to evening, some began to despair of finding the Lance . . . The youth who had spoken of the Lance, however, upon seeing us worn out, disrobed and, taking off his shoes, descended into the pit in his shirt, earnestly entreating us to pray to God to give us His Lance for the comfort and victory of His people. At length, the Lord was minded through the grace of His mercy to show us His Lance. And I, who have written this, kissed it when the point alone had as yet appeared above ground. What great joy then filled the city I cannot describe.

Source C: from Jonathan Riley-Smith, *The First Crusade and the Idea of Crusading* (1990).

The strangest of the discoveries was the Holy Lance which had pierced Christ's side during the crucifixion. A Southern French serving-man called Peter Bartholomew claimed to have had a vision of St. Andrew, who transported him into the church of St. Peter and produced the Holy Lance from a spot on the floor . . . There was . . . open scepticism, even hostility, shown by other leaders. There was, after all, a well known Holy Lance already in Constantinople. Adhemar of Le Puy's reaction was that of any good bishop to extraordinary claims and fervour; he openly expressed his doubts. So did Arnulf of Chocques and the bishop of Apt. Robert of Normandy, Robert of Flanders, Tancred and Bohemond were all very sceptical believing that Peter had simply brought a piece of iron with him into the cathedral.

Source D: from the *Alexiad* by Anna Comnena, written in 1140.

For he [Bohemond] was quick, and a man of very dishonest disposition. Although inferior to all the Latins who had crossed over into Asia, he was more malicious and courageous than any of them. But even though he thus excelled all in great cunning, the inconstant character of the Latins was also in him. Truly, the riches which he spurned at first, he now gladly accepted. For when this man of evil design had left his country in which he possessed no wealth at all (under the pretext, indeed, of adoring at the Lord's Sepulchre, but in reality trying to acquire for himself a kingdom), he found himself in need of much money, especially, indeed, if he was to seize the Roman power. In this he followed the advice of his father and, so to speak, was leaving no stone unturned.

Source E: from Christopher Tyerman, *The Invention of the Crusades* (1998).

As crusading became increasingly associated with papal wars in Italy in the fourteenth century, so there was a shift in criticism. Critics of wars within Christendom, even those under the guise of crusaders, persisted for as long as those wars continued . . . Advice presented to the Council of Lyon in 1274 had confirmed that there was hostility to political crusades and that a mixture of distraction, indifference and laziness stood in the path of new Holy Land Crusades. However, inertia and European wars, not the outcries of critics, crippled attempts by Gregory X to organise a new crusade.

[*END OF SOURCES FOR SPECIAL TOPIC 2*]

SPECIAL TOPIC 2: THE CRUSADES 1096–1204

Answer *all* of the following questions.

Marks

1. How valuable is **Source A** as evidence that religion was important in influencing people to go on crusade?
    In reaching a conclusion you should refer to:
    *   *the origin and possible purpose of the source;*
    *   *the content of the source;*
    *   *recalled knowledge.*   **5**

2. Compare the views expressed in **Sources B** and **C** about the discovery of the Holy Lance.
    Compare the sources overall and in detail.   **5**

3. How well does **Source D** illustrate the character of Bohemond as a crusading leader?
    Use the source and recalled knowledge.   **6**

4. How fully do **Sources A**, **B** and **D** demonstrate the motives of those who went on crusade?
    *Use **Sources A, B** and **D** and recalled knowledge.*   **8**

5. How far does **Source E** describe the decline of the crusading ideal?
    Use the source and recalled knowledge.   **6**

(30)

[*END OF QUESTIONS ON SPECIAL TOPIC 2*]

OPTION B: EARLY MODERN HISTORY

SPECIAL TOPIC 3: SCOTLAND 1689–1715

Study the sources below and then answer the questions which follow.

Source A: from P. H. Scott, *Andrew Fletcher and the Treaty of Union* (1992).

It was the question of the succession to the throne which brought the relationship between the two countries to a critical point which had to be resolved one way or another. On 30 July 1700, William, duke of Gloucester, the last survivor of Queen Anne's eighteen children, died. There was no longer any obvious and automatic heir to the throne. The legitimate line of descent from James VII and II, the Jacobite Pretender, could not be re-established without overthrowing the Protestant settlement of the "Glorious Revolution". The English Parliament, again with no consultation with Scotland, in the Act of Succession of 1701, offered the throne to the Protestant Sophia, Electress of Hanover, and her descendants . . . The English Parliament seems to have assumed that Scotland would meekly accept their decision. In fact, their high-handed action called in question the survival of the union of the two monarchies which had come about in 1603. For all these reasons, the relationship with England reached a critical point in the early years of Anne's reign.

Source B: from a speech by Lord Belhaven on the first Article of the Treaty, 2 November 1706.

I shall remind this honourable House, that we are the successors of our noble forefathers, who founded our monarchy, framed our laws, without the assistance or advice of any foreign power or ruler; and who, during the time of two thousand years have handed them down to us, a free and independent nation . . . Shall we not then argue for that which our forefathers have purchased for us so dearly, and with so much immortal honour and glory? God forbid . . . if our descendants, after we are dead and gone, shall find themselves under an ill-made bargain . . . they will certainly say, "Ah! Our nation has been reduced to the last extremity at the time of this treaty; all our great men who in the past defended the rights and liberties of the nation, have all been killed and lie dead in the bed of honour, before ever the nation was reduced to agree to such contemptible terms . . . They have certainly all been extinguished, and now we are slaves for ever".

Source C: from George Lockhart of Carnwath, *Scotland's Ruine* (1714).

But the Equivalent was the mighty bait, for here with the sum of three hundred and ninety one thousand and eighty five pounds sterling to be sent in cash to Scotland. However, the Scots were to pay it and much more back again in a few years by agreeing to bear a share of the burdens imposed on England and used for payment of England's debts . . . This may chiefly explain why so many of them agreed to this union. The hopes of recovering what they had spent on the Company of Scotland, and of paying debts and arrears due to them . . . made many overlook the general interest of their country.

Source D: from Rosalind Mitchison, *Lordship to Patronage* (1983).

Enough of such a machinery already existed to smooth the conduct of affairs, yet in fact the distribution of honours and money on this occasion was small. Some peerages were given, and some payment of arrears and salary, amounting in all to £20,000, were secretly made. The sums were small even in the terms in which the parliamentary classes worked . . . Their smallness suggests that they really were arrears and not bribes. The main offer which the English dominated government could make to Scottish politicians was of course a share in power, and about this there were reservations not yet apparent . . .

It was still necessary to get the volatile Scottish Parliament to agree to the treaty. A vital step in the process was to be an Act assuring the Scottish Church establishment.

Source E: from an early eighteenth-century Jacobite song "Caledon, O Caledon how wretched is thy fate?"

> In Days of Yore you were renowned,
> Conspicuous was your fame,
> All nations did your Valour Praise,
> And Loyalty Proclaim;
>
> You did your Ancient Rights maintain,
> And Liberties defend,
> And scorned to have it thought that you
> On England did depend.
>
> Unto your Kings you did adhere,
> Stood by the Royal Race;
> With them you honour great did gain,
> And Paths of Glory trace;
> With Royal Stewart at your Head
> All enemies oppose,
> And like our brave Courageous Clans,
> In Pieces cut your foes . . .

[END OF SOURCES FOR SPECIAL TOPIC 3]

SPECIAL TOPIC 3: SCOTLAND 1689–1715

Answer *all* of the following questions.

Marks

1. To what extent does **Source A** explain why relations between Scotland and England became worse in the period 1690–1705?
    Use the source and recalled knowledge.　　**7**

2. How useful is **Source B** as evidence of opposition in Scotland towards the Union?
    In reaching a conclusion you should refer to:
    *   *the origin and possible purpose of the source;*
    *   *the content of the source;*
    *   *recalled knowledge.*　　**5**

3. Compare the views expressed in **Sources C** and **D** on the importance of financial incentives in passing the Act of Union.
    Compare the sources overall and in detail.　　**4**

4. To what extent do **Sources A, C** and **D** explain why the Act of Union was passed?
    *Use **Sources A, C** and **D** and recalled knowledge.*　　**8**

5. How typical is **Source E** of the views of Scottish opponents of the Union in the period after 1707?
    Use the source and recalled knowledge.　　**6**

　　(30)

[END OF QUESTIONS ON SPECIAL TOPIC 3]

SPECIAL TOPIC 4: THE ATLANTIC SLAVE TRADE

Study the sources below and then answer the questions which follow.

Source A: from the evidence of Alexander Falconbridge, a surgeon who served on Slave ships, to a Parliamentary Committee, 1790.

The men Negroes, on being brought aboard ship, are immediately fastened together two and two, by handcuffs on their wrists, and by irons riveted on their legs . . . They are frequently stowed so close as to allow no other posture than lying on their sides. Neither will the height between the decks, unless directly under the grating, permit them to stand, especially where there are platforms, which is generally the case. These platforms are a kind of shelf, about eight or nine feet in breadth, extending from the side of the ship towards the centre. They are placed nearly midway between the decks, at the distance of two or three feet from each deck. Upon these the Negroes are stowed in the same manner as they are on the deck underneath.

Source B: "a black on yellow Jasper Slave Medallion made in the Etruria factory of Josiah Wedgwood in support of the anti-slavery campaign."

Source C: from Peter J. Kitson, *Slavery, Abolition and Emancipation: Volume 2 – The Abolition Debate* (1999).

Various arguments that circulated in support of the trade usually originated from the Society of West India Planters and the merchants of London, Bristol and Liverpool. This propaganda was financed by a levy on West Indian imports into the port of London and was strongly backed by the MPs. From the start there was little attempt at a moral justification of the trade . . . By and large the pro-slavery propagandists stressed the economic argument. While reform of the plantations was necessary, abolition would simply mean handing over the trade to competitor nations. A common argument was that in many ways the slaves were better off than the labouring poor in Britain. Slavery was defended as a necessary evil that had always existed. Jamaica and the other West Indian islands were not able to sustain an increasing slave population and therefore relied on the trade for essential labour.

Source D: from Samuel Taylor Coleridge, *On the Slave Trade* (1796).

It has been asserted by more than one writer on the subject that the plantation slaves are at least as well off as the peasantry in England. Now I appeal to common sense, whether to affirm that the slaves are as well off as our peasantry is not the same as to assert that our peasantry are as badly off as Negro slaves? And whether if our peasantry believed it, they would not be inclined to rebel?

[It is said] that the slaves are more humanely treated and live more happily in the plantations than in their native country. If any person should entertain a doubt of this, the slave-merchants, slave-holders, and slave-drivers together with the manufacturers of neck-collars and thumbscrews, are ready and willing to take their bible oaths on it! When treated with tolerable humanity the human race, as well as other animals, multiplies. The Negroes multiply in their native country: they do *not* multiply in the West Indian islands; for if they did, the slave trade would have been abolished long ago by its lack of usefulness.

Source E: from James Walvin, "Public Campaign in England", in D. Eltis and J. Walvin (eds), *The Abolition of the Atlantic Slave Trade* (1981).

The emergence of popular radicalism (English Jacobinism to its enemies) . . . transformed the political climate in England. War with France in 1793, and the disintegration in Haiti (with the loss of thousands of British troops in a forlorn campaign against former slaves in that island), did nothing to help the abolitionist cause . . . Popular associations, petitions, cheap publications, public lectures, large public meetings, pressure on Parliament: these, the lifeblood of abolitionism, were now adopted by the radicals. And in the process these came to be resisted as a potentially disastrous repeat of events in France.

[END OF SOURCES FOR SPECIAL TOPIC 4]

SPECIAL TOPIC 4: THE ATLANTIC SLAVE TRADE

Answer *all* of the following questions.

Marks

1. How valuable is **Source A** as evidence of conditions on the Middle Passage?
   In reaching a conclusion you should refer to:
   * *the origin and possible purpose of the source;*
   * *the content of the source;*
   * *recalled knowledge.*   **5**

2. How typical is **Source B** of the methods used by abolitionists?
   Use the source and recalled knowledge.   **6**

3. To what extent does **Source C** identify the arguments used by supporters of the Slave Trade?
   Use the source and recalled knowledge.   **6**

4. How far does **Source D** support the pro-slavery arguments outlined in **Source C**?
   Compare the sources overall and in detail.   **5**

5. How fully do **Sources C**, **D** and **E** explain the difficulties faced by abolitionists in their campaign?
   *Use **Sources C, D** and **E** and recalled knowledge.*   **8**

                                                                                            (30)

[END OF QUESTIONS ON SPECIAL TOPIC 4]

SPECIAL TOPIC 5: THE AMERICAN REVOLUTION

Study the sources below and then answer the questions which follow.

Source A: from a letter from Joseph Reed of Philadelphia to the earl of Dartmouth, American Secretary, June 1774.

I cannot think myself a rebel or a traitor. I love my king, respect the Parliament, and have the highest regard for the mother country, and these are the sentiments of every important person with whom I speak . . . But if the Port of Boston Bill and the other proceedings against that province have been founded on a supposition that the other colonies would leave them to struggle alone, I do assure your Lordship there never was a greater mistake.

Source B: from a speech in Parliament by Lord North on the Port of Boston Bill, 1774.

We are now disputing, not I trust with all the Colonies, but with those who have maintained that we have as a Parliament no legislative right over them and that we are two independent states under the same king . . . We are not entering into a dispute between internal and external taxes, not between taxes levied for the purposes of revenue and taxes levied for the regulation of trade, not between representation and taxation, or legislation and taxation. But we are now to dispute the question whether we have or have not any authority in that country.

Source C: from Peter D. G. Thomas, *Revolution in America* (1992).

The root cause of the American Revolution was the question of whether or not Parliament was the legislature for the British Empire. Public discussion of the constitutional relationship between Britain and her colonies was stimulated from 1763 because government measures increasingly took the form of Parliamentary legislation instead of executive action by the Crown. Parliamentary sovereignty over Britain's overseas possessions had been assumed rather than frequently exercised or asserted. The colonial challenge during the Stamp Act Crisis led to the Declaratory Act of 1766, the first formal claim of full Parliamentary power over the Colonies. It took some time for the colonists to dispute this outright . . . The first practical exertion of complete Parliamentary power occurred with the legislation of 1774. That led to a direct colonial challenge to Parliament's power of legislation. It was an implicit demand for internal home rule under the Crown, and a claim quite incompatible with the greatest concession any British politician would make.

Source D: from Ray Raphael, *The American Revolution, A People's History* (2001).

On May 31, 1774, Philip Vickers Fithian from the Northern Neck of Virginia recorded in his journal: "The lower class of people here are agitated by the account of reports from Boston, many of them expect to be pressed and compelled to go and fight the British!" Not that these common folk were unpatriotic: when the alarm sounded a year later, they joined companies of volunteers in great numbers. But they didn't want to be forced into service. They didn't want to leave their homes for extended periods of time, nor to take orders from men who claimed to be their superiors.

In the spring and summer of 1775, during the height of the military fever, plain farmers from Virginia seized control of the volunteer companies which had originally been formed by gentry . . . They insisted on voting for their own officers. As volunteers, they also insisted on the right to come or leave as they pleased.

Source E: from "Derry Down", a British song from the time of the American Revolution.

America . . .
Now finds she's being used by both France and Spain,
Yet all three united can't weigh down the scale,
So the Dutchman jumps in with the hope to prevail.
Derry down, down, down, derry down
Yet Britain will boldly their efforts withstand,
And bravely defy them by sea and by land.

[END OF SOURCES FOR SPECIAL TOPIC 5]

SPECIAL TOPIC 5: THE AMERICAN REVOLUTION

Answer *all* of the following questions.

Marks

1. How valuable is **Source A** as evidence of the colonists' attitude to Britain in the years before the outbreak of war?
   In reaching a conclusion you should refer to:
   • *the origin and possible purpose of the source;*
   • *the content of the source;*
   • *recalled knowledge.*   **5**

2. To what extent does the evidence in **Source B** support the analysis in **Source C** of the nature of the dispute between Britain and the Colonies?
   Compare the sources overall and in detail.   **5**

3. How fully do **Sources A**, **B** and **C** reveal the reasons for the colonial challenge to British control in America?
   *Use **Sources A, B and C** and recalled knowledge.*   **8**

4. How important are the issues raised in **Source D** in understanding the problems faced by the Continental army after the outbreak of war?
   Use the source and recalled knowledge.   **6**

5. How accurately does **Source E** assess the significance of foreign intervention in the American War of Independence?
   Use the source and recalled knowledge.   **6**

                                                                            (30)

[END OF QUESTIONS ON SPECIAL TOPIC 5]

OPTION C: LATER MODERN HISTORY

SPECIAL TOPIC 6: PATTERNS OF MIGRATION: SCOTLAND 1830s–1930s

Study the sources below and then answer the questions which follow.

Source A: from a *Report on the Condition of the Poorer Classes of Edinburgh and their Dwellings, Neighbourhoods and Families* (1868).

In the Middle Meal Market Stairs are 59 rooms entered by a steep, dark, stone stair, common to all. In these dwell 248 individuals, divided into 56 families. And in these dens there is no water, no water-closet, no sink. The women living on the fifth or highest floor have to carry all their water up the close and up these stairs. It is not difficult to imagine the state of wet and filth in which they must continually be. In Birtley Buildings in the Canongate a similar picture exists. These are not exceptional cases; there are hundreds of others as bad; indeed, the census for 1861 brought out distinctly that in Edinburgh there were actually 13,209 families living in a single room, more than one third of our whole population. It appears that more than 900 of these were cellars, most of them damp and totally dark. It must not be supposed that these 13,209 families are the immoral and abject poor alone. Among them are to be found nearly all our common labouring classes, a great many of whom are of Irish stock.

Source B: from the report of the Education Commission (Scotland) (1866).

The people in the Clyde district are of the poorest classes and this district has a large mixture of Irish immigrants. For this large Irish element and their needs there exists no school within the district, beyond a private adventure school in one of the wynds. Roman Catholic children are indeed to be found in the other schools but in comparatively small numbers and their attendance is extremely irregular. It is a fact that many children in the Clyde district, both Catholic and Protestant, but chiefly the former, attend no school. What are these neglected children doing, then, if they are selling matches and running errands, cared for by no-one, not at school? They are idling in the streets and wynds, tumbling about in the gutters.

Source C: from W. Hamish Fraser and R. J. Morris (eds), *People and Society in Scotland Vol.II, 1830–1914* (1990).

The uneven pace of an industrialising and urbanising society was reflected in distinctive religious, cultural and educational divisions. The largest number of schools, pupils and teachers was to be found in Glasgow, but many of those were Catholic schools outside the state system. Irish settlement, especially after the Famine, produced an ever-growing demand for Catholic schools and teachers. Nonetheless, by the 1860s, the Catholic clergy could boast that they had overcome the immense difficulties and could offer pupils instruction in the three Rs and the Bible. But the community lacked the resources to pay adequate school fees or to raise the necessary funds towards teachers' salaries and school buildings. As a result, by the end of the century, there was a growing crisis in Catholic education.

Source D: from J. A. Jackson, *The Irish in Britain* (1963).

The success of the Irish settlement in Britain is concealed by placing undue emphasis on the problems with which the Irish have been associated and on the clashes of religion and temperament which have occurred between the immigrants and native population. The typical pattern of settlement, consolidation and gradual assimilation into the host community is told in the far less dramatic life history of individuals and families. Gradually the immigrant found his voice in the Press and in politics. He found and fought for his power in the labour movement; through benevolent societies he achieved economic security. He found comfort and support in the clubs and associations dedicated to his own culture.

Source E: from a letter from Michie Ewing from Canada to Colonel Charles Fraser, 1857.

It is now nearly two years since we left and God in his mercy has blessed us with remarkable good health in our adopted country. And although I have not been altogether so successful as I expected, yet I like the country, I like the climate and I am fully convinced that many a poor man would be much better here than in Scotland. Yet there are many who come here who would be much better at home than here. Wages are high, but much more work is expected and unless a man is a good workman few will employ him. A good many get disheartened and return home, go drinking or even lose their health and die. Yet, I have great cause to be thankful in that all the time I have had plenty of work and sometimes two or three persons wanting me at the one time.

[*END OF SOURCES FOR SPECIAL TOPIC 6*]

SPECIAL TOPIC 6: PATTERNS OF MIGRATION: SCOTLAND 1830s–1930s

Answer *all* of the following questions.

Marks

1. How useful is **Source A** as evidence of the living conditions experienced by Irish immigrants to Scotland?
   In reaching a conclusion you should refer to:
   * *the origin and possible purpose of the source;*
   * *the content of the source;*
   * *recalled knowledge.*   **5**

2. Compare the views of **Sources B** and **C** concerning the provision of education for Irish immigrants to Scotland.
   Compare the sources overall and in detail.   **5**

3. How successfully did other European immigrants preserve their identity in similar ways to the Irish as outlined in **Source D**?
   Use the source and recalled knowledge.   **6**

4. Assess the impact of Irish immigrants on Scottish society between 1830 and 1930.
   *Use **Sources B**, **C** and **D** and recalled knowledge.*   **8**

5. How typical of the experiences of emigrant Scots are those described in **Source E**?
   Use the source and recalled knowledge.   **6**

(30)

[*END OF QUESTIONS ON SPECIAL TOPIC 6*]

SPECIAL TOPIC 7: APPEASEMENT AND THE ROAD TO WAR, TO 1939

Study the sources below and then answer the questions which follow.

Source A: from minutes of a meeting of the British Cabinet, 11 March 1936.

From information given by the Service Ministers it is clear that our position at home and in home waters is a disadvantageous one whether from the point of view of the Navy, Army or Air Force or anti-aircraft defence. In addition, public opinion is strongly opposed to any military action against the Germans in the demilitarised zone. In particular, the ex-servicemen are very anti-French. Moreover, many people, perhaps most people, are openly saying that they do not see why the Germans should not reoccupy the Rhineland. In these circumstances it is generally accepted that it is worth taking almost any risk in order to escape from that situation.

Source B: a drawing from the *Illustrated London News*, published in 1937, showing ways in which the Royal Air Force was rearming as part of a five-year plan.

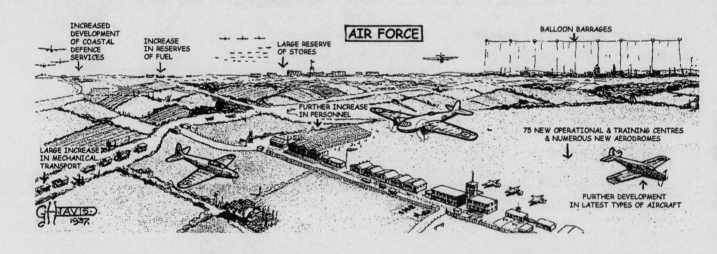

Source C: from the record kept by Dr. Kurt Schuschnigg, the Chancellor of Austria, of his meeting with Adolf Hitler, 12 February 1938.

Schuschnigg – Naturally, I realise that you can march into Austria, but . . . whether we wish it or not, that would lead to the shedding of blood. We are not alone in the world. That probably means war.

Hitler – Will you take the responsibility for that, Herr Schuschnigg? Don't believe that the world will hinder me in my decisions. Italy? I am quite clear with Mussolini; with Italy I am on the closest possible terms. England? England will not lift a finger for Austria . . . and France? Well, two years ago when we marched into the Rhineland with a handful of battalions—at that moment I risked a great deal. If France had marched then we should have been forced to withdraw . . . But for France it is now too late.

Source D: from the leading article, *Glasgow Herald*, 14 March 1938.

It is time for Britain's rulers to make up their minds clearly and unmistakably about the position we are ready to take up in Europe and the world. That is the plain message of what has happened in Austria. Europe is faced with a type of political leadership which will be bound by no ordinary promises, which is ready to use force to the utmost when the indecision or weakness of peacefully minded powers leaves the way to violence open. In this matter the rights and wrongs of the Anschluss itself are beside the point.

All that matters are the attitudes of Nazi Germany towards agreements freely made by its leaders and their lack of sincerity in dealing with friendly governments such as our own. In face of these things, are we to adopt the ideas of the isolationists, abandon all active interest in Europe and prepare to defend unaided our own territories and trade throughout all the world? Or are we to lay down the limit beyond which we shall not be prepared to allow the forcible remaking of Europe to proceed? No British government has made it clear either to ourselves or to the rest of the world just what we propose to do if France were to be drawn into a war by her continental alliances.

Source E: from Piers Brendon, *The Dark Valley* (2000).

With surprising speed a reaction set in against Munich. Feelings of joy at Britain's deliverance from war were overtaken by feelings of shame at the betrayal of Czechoslovakia. What had seemed a brave bid for peace in September appeared, as autumn progressed, to be a fatal act of cowardice in the face of alien strength. By 320 votes to 266 the Oxford Union carried a motion deploring "the Government's policy of peace with honour". On Bonfire Night . . . a "guy" was burned dressed in a black Homburg hat and a frock coat, complete with a neatly rolled umbrella. The government did badly in by-elections and china ornaments celebrating Chamberlain the peace-maker remained unsold in shops.

[END OF SOURCES FOR SPECIAL TOPIC 7]

SPECIAL TOPIC 7: APPEASEMENT AND THE ROAD TO WAR, TO 1939

Answer *all* of the following questions.   *Marks*

1. How fully does **Source A** explain the British reaction to the remilitarisation of the Rhineland?
    Use the source and recalled knowledge.   **6**

2. Compare the evidence in **Sources A** and **B** about the condition of the British armed forces in the late 1930s.
    Compare the sources overall and in detail.   **5**

3. How useful is **Source C** as evidence of Hitler's attitude towards Britain and France at the time of the Anschluss?
    In reaching a conclusion you should refer to:
    *   *the origin and possible purpose of the source;*
    *   *the content of the source;*
    *   *recalled knowledge.*   **5**

4. To what extent does **Source D** reflect British public opinion about the Anschluss?
    Use the source and recalled knowledge.   **6**

5. How effective was the policy of appeasement in achieving its objectives?
    *Use **Sources C, D** and **E** and recalled knowledge.*   **8**

                                                                                                (30)

[END OF QUESTIONS ON SPECIAL TOPIC 7]

SPECIAL TOPIC 8: THE ORIGINS AND DEVELOPMENT OF THE COLD WAR 1945–1985

Study the sources below and then answer the questions which follow.

Source A: from a television broadcast by Walther Ulbricht, leader of the German Democratic Republic, 18 August 1961.

Eventful days lie behind us. The workers, and all the people of the German Democratic Republic, can breathe a sigh of relief . . . With growing anger, they had seen how they were being made fools of and robbed by the militarist rabble of the government in West Germany . . .

The Bonn government has rejected all our peaceful proposals. Their War Minister has ordered a speed-up in the atomic armament of their army, which is commanded by former Nazi generals . . .

We know their plans. They were aimed at creating conditions that would allow an open attack against the GDR and create civil war . . .

It was clear that a very dangerous situation had arisen for peace in Europe and the world. In order to remove this danger to the peace of our people and other peoples, we contacted our friends at an early date and agreed to take action against it.

Source B: from a statement to the West German Parliament by Konrad Adenauer, Chancellor of the Federal Republic of West Germany, 18 August 1961.

The Federal Government considers it essential to draw the attention of world public opinion to the true causes of this crisis . . .

It is not any militaristic or revenge-seeking policies by the Federal Government that have caused the rulers of the Soviet zone of Germany to take this action. It is the result of their refusal to let the people of the Soviet-occupied zone of Germany live according to the way of life which they desire . . .

The permanent flow of refugees in recent weeks tells a different story—the true story . . . In their desperation, they saw no other way out than to leave their homes in the Soviet-occupied zone . . . to begin a new life in freedom in the Federal Republic. There was nothing left for them but to "vote with their feet".

Source C: from J. Isaacs and T. Downing, *The Cold War* (1998).

When Nikita Khrushchev stood up to address the delegates of the Twenty Second Communist Party Congress in Moscow, he had something special to tell them . . . He announced that the Soviet Union had just detonated the largest bomb the world had ever seen—equivalent to more than 50 million tons of TNT . . . This heralded a new generation of Soviet superbombs.

Khrushchev told the party members that he hoped "we are never called upon to explode these bombs over anybody's territory". Khrushchev neatly summed up the Cold War's nuclear paradox. Each side devoted huge sums to developing weapons it hoped never to use.

Source D: from "What Lies Ahead", a newspaper article by Josef Smrkovsky, a leading supporter of the reform movement in Czechoslovakia, 9 February 1968.

The Central Committee of the party has attempted to find the cause of the tameness and indifference in our country . . . There is a conviction growing that there must be a basic change of course. Such a change must be aimed at the democratisation of the party and society as a whole . . . It must be backed by realistic guarantees that are understood by the majority of the people.

That is why the Central Committee has decided to draw up an Action Programme and start work on a project for the advancement of socialist society . . . We shall find no ready made solutions. It is up to us, both Czechs and Slovaks, to launch out into unexplored territory and search for a Czechoslovak road to socialism.

Source E: from a statement by the Central Committee of the Communist Party of the Soviet Union, 19 August 1968.

In recent days, events in Czechoslovakia have assumed a most ominous character . . . Right-wing forces have attempted to force the party and government of Czechoslovakia to follow a pro-Western policy and return Czechoslovakia to a bourgeois republic . . .

We have concluded that the moment has arrived to undertake active measures in defence of socialism in Czechoslovakia . . .

We have ordered our military units to take all necessary measures on 21 August to help the Czechoslovak working people in their struggle against reactionary forces and to protect their security against the intrigues of imperialism . . . Our enemies should be fully aware that no-one . . . will ever be permitted to break a single link in the community of socialist states.

[*END OF SOURCES FOR SPECIAL TOPIC 8*]

SPECIAL TOPIC 8: THE ORIGINS AND DEVELOPMENT OF THE COLD WAR 1945–1985

Answer *all* of the following questions.

Marks

1. How valuable is **Source A** as evidence of East Germany's attitude towards West Berlin at this time?
   In reaching a conclusion you should refer to:
   * *the origin and possible purpose of the source;*
   * *the content of the source;*
   * *recalled knowledge.*   **5**

2. Compare the views of the Berlin Crisis of 1961 given in **Sources A** and **B**.
   Compare the sources overall and in detail.   **5**

3. How far do you accept the views in **Source C** on the development of the nuclear arms race?
   Use the source and recalled knowledge.   **6**

4. How fully does **Source D** illustrate the growing demand for reform in Czechoslovakia in the 1960s?
   Use the source and recalled knowledge.   **6**

5. To what extent do **Sources A**, **C** and **E** explain the issues which divided the Superpowers during the Cold War?
   *Use **Sources A, C** and **E** and recalled knowledge.*   **8**

   (30)

[*END OF QUESTIONS ON SPECIAL TOPIC 8*]

SPECIAL TOPIC 9: IRELAND 1900–1985: A DIVIDED IDENTITY

Study the sources below and then answer the questions which follow.

Source A: from a speech by Winston Churchill, a Government Minister, at Celtic Park Football Ground, Belfast, 8 February 1912.

I come to you on the eve of a Home Rule Bill. We intend to place before Parliament our plan for the better government of Ireland . . . We have consulted, and we shall consult fully, with the leaders of Irish public opinion, but the decision rests with us . . .

The bill which we shall introduce will be a bill of a British Government designed to smooth the path of the British Empire, and liberate new forces for its services . . . For more than twenty-five years, Home Rule has been the policy of the Liberal Party. Liberals have been taught to believe that the best solution of Irish difficulties lies in the establishment of an Irish Parliament with an Executive responsible to it.

Source B: a cartoon published in 1914, showing John Redmond.

Source C: from Robert Kee, *The Green Flag* (1972).

The speed with which the election of 1918 was called acted in Sinn Féin's favour . . . Very many soldiers had not received their postal voting papers . . . It seems probable that many of them would have voted for the old Nationalist Party, rather than for Sinn Féin, still thought of as pro-German . . .

Sinn Féin was also much favoured in the election by the greatly enlarged new register, which almost trebled the previous Irish electorate . . .

Another telling factor was that Sinn Féin already seemed to be the winning party. In 26 constituencies, the Nationalist Party could not even find a candidate . . . Probably what most Sinn Féin voters were voting for was simply the greatest measure of independence, without partition of the country, which Ireland could get. The one thing they were certainly not voting for was an attempt to win independence by force of arms or a campaign of terrorism.

Source D: from a press statement by Eamonn de Valera, June 1922.

English propaganda will strive to lay the blame for this war on Irishmen, but the world outside must not be deceived. England's threat of war alone is responsible for the present situation.

In face of England's threat of war, some of our countrymen yielded. The men who are now being attacked by the forces of the Provisional Government are those who refuse to obey the order to yield—preferring to die. They are the best and bravest of our nation, and would most loyally have obeyed the will of the Irish people freely expressed. They are not willing that Ireland's independence should be abandoned under the lash of a foreign government.

Source E: from notes made by Michael Collins, August 1922.

Our opponents claim to be opposing the National Government which they declare to have seized power illegally. In view of the elections, this is absurd . . . And what are they complaining of? . . . Simply that the Government refused to let authority be wrested from it by an armed minority . . . We saw them pursuing exactly the same course as the English Black and Tans . . .

There is no British Government any longer in Ireland. It is gone. It is no longer the enemy. We have now our own government, constitutionally elected, and it is the duty of every Irish man and woman to obey it. Anyone who fails to obey it is an enemy of the people and must expect to be treated as such.

[END OF SOURCES FOR SPECIAL TOPIC 9]

SPECIAL TOPIC 9: IRELAND 1900–1985: A DIVIDED IDENTITY

Answer *all* of the following questions.

Marks

1. How effective was the policy of Home Rule, as outlined in **Source A**, in addressing the concerns of the Irish people at the time?
   Use the source and recalled knowledge.　　6

2. How useful is **Source B** as evidence of the difficulties in carrying out the policy of Home Rule?
   In reaching a conclusion you should refer to:
   • *the origin and possible purpose of the source;*
   • *the content of the source;*
   • *recalled knowledge.*　　5

3. To what extent does **Source C** explain the reasons for the victory of Sinn Féin in the election of 1918?
   Use the source and recalled knowledge.　　6

4. Compare the views in **Sources D** and **E** on the reasons for the outbreak of the Irish Civil War.
   Compare the sources overall and in detail.　　5

5. How fully do **Sources B, C** and **E** illustrate the development of division and conflict in Ireland between 1912 and 1922?
   *Use **Sources B, C** and **E** and recalled knowledge.*　　8

(30)

[END OF QUESTIONS ON SPECIAL TOPIC 9]

[END OF QUESTION PAPER]

[BLANK PAGE]

2006 | Higher

[BLANK PAGE]

X044/301

NATIONAL
QUALIFICATIONS
2006

MONDAY, 22 MAY
9.00 AM – 10.20 AM

HISTORY
HIGHER
Paper 1

Answer questions on **one** Option only.

Take particular care to show clearly the Option chosen. On the **front** of the answer book, **in the top right-hand corner**, write A or B or C.

Within the Option chosen, answer **two** questions, one from Historical Study: Scottish and British and one from Historical Study: European and World.

All questions are assigned 25 marks.

Marks may be deducted for bad spelling and bad punctuation, and for writing that is difficult to read.

SCOTTISH
QUALIFICATIONS
AUTHORITY

[BLANK PAGE]

OPTION A: MEDIEVAL HISTORY

**Answer TWO questions, one from Historical Study: Scottish and British
and one from Historical Study: European and World**

Historical Study: Scottish and British

Medieval Society

1. How difficult were the lives of the peasants, both free and un-free, in twelfth-century Scotland and England?

2. "The medieval Church was interested mainly in secular power. Religion came a poor second." Discuss.

3. How far do you agree that towns were a vital part of medieval society?

4. To what extent was there a "Norman colonisation" of Scotland during the reign of David I?

5. Discuss the view that the quarrel between Henry II and Thomas Becket was nothing more than a clash of personalities.

Historical Study: European and World

EITHER

Nation and King

6. "It was King John's unpleasant personality that led to the baronial opposition and Magna Carta." How far do you agree with this statement?

7. To what extent was Philip II a successful monarch?

8. To what extent did a community of the realm develop in Scotland during the period 1286–1298?

9. How important was the Battle of Bannockburn in ensuring Scottish victory in the Wars of Independence?

OR

Crisis of Authority

10. "The Hundred Years' War was fought mainly to decide whether kings of England should still hold lands in France as vassals of the French king." Discuss.

11. To what extent was the poll tax of 1380 the major cause of the Peasants' Revolt of 1381?

12. Why was the Conciliar Movement (1409–1449) unable to solve fully the problems facing the Church at the start of the fifteenth century?

13. To what extent was there a crisis of authority in Europe in the fourteenth and fifteenth centuries?

OPTION B: EARLY MODERN HISTORY

Answer TWO questions, one from Historical Study: Scottish and British and one from Historical Study: European and World

Historical Study: Scottish and British

EITHER

Scotland in the Age of the Reformation 1542–1603

1. What was the most serious weakness of the Church before 1560?

2. To what extent did rivalry between England and France dominate Scottish politics between 1542 and 1560?

3. "Selfish and greedy nobles made Scotland impossible to rule." How important was this as a reason for Mary, Queen of Scots, losing her throne?

4. How important was the establishment of law and order to the success of James VI's reign in Scotland?

5. Do you consider that religious issues were the main cause of conflict in Scotland between 1542 and 1603?

OR

Scotland and England in the Century of Revolutions 1603–1702

6. "Financial issues caused the most serious challenges to the authority of James I in England after 1603." How far do you agree?

7. Why did Charles I find it so difficult to rule Scotland?

8. To what extent was religion the main cause of the Civil War in England?

9. Why did Cromwell fail to find an acceptable form of government for England in the 1650s?

10. "The Glorious Revolution was the climax to the Parliamentary challenge to royal authority in the seventeenth century." Discuss.

Historical Study: European and World

EITHER

Royal Authority in 17th and 18th Century Europe

11. How important was Louis XIV's personal role in the government of France?

12. "A disastrous failure." How accurate is this description of Louis XIV's treatment of religious minorities in France?

13. "Frederick II of Prussia was more interested in efficient government than in the welfare of his people." How far do you agree?

14. "Here lies a king who failed in all he tried to do." Was Joseph II fair to himself in writing this epitaph?

OR

The French Revolution: The Emergence of the Citizen State

15. To what extent were the grievances of the peasants a threat to the Ancien Régime?

16. Explain why the revolt of the nobles in 1787 resulted in violent revolution by 1789.

17. "The flight of Louis XVI to Varennes guaranteed the end of the monarchy." How far do you agree?

18. Why was there so much instability in France between 1793 and 1799?

[Turn over

OPTION C: LATER MODERN HISTORY

**Answer TWO questions, one from Historical Study: Scottish and British
and one from Historical Study: European and World**

Historical Study: Scottish and British

Britain 1850s–1979

1. Discuss the view that by 1914 Britain was not yet a democratic country.

2. To what extent did the social reforms of the Liberal Government (1906–1914) improve the lives of the British people?

3. How important were socialist societies in the growth of the Labour Party by 1906?

4. "The National Government (1931–1940) has been criticised most unfairly for its economic policies." How far would you agree?

5. **Either**

   (*a*) To what extent did urbanisation benefit the people of Scotland during the period 1880–1939?

   Or

   (*b*) How far did varying levels of support for the Scottish National Party between 1945 and 1979 result from changes in the Scottish economy?

Historical Study: European and World

EITHER

The Growth of Nationalism

6. Why was unification achieved in Germany **or** Italy?

7. **Either**

    (*a*) To what extent was national unity a problem within Germany between 1871 and 1914?

    Or

    (*b*) What was the most serious difficulty the new Italian state faced between 1871 and 1914?

8. "Resentment towards the peace treaties at the end of the First World War made the rise of fascism inevitable." Discuss with reference to **either** Germany **or** Italy.

9. "Totalitarian rule benefited most of the people." Do you agree with this opinion about **either** Germany between 1933 and 1939 **or** Italy between 1922 and 1939?

OR

The Large Scale State

The USA

10. How important was the Ku Klux Klan in causing the problems facing black Americans during the 1920s and 1930s?

11. Why did some Americans not share in the general economic prosperity of the 1920s?

12. How effective were the increased powers of the federal government in dealing with the social and economic problems facing the USA in the 1930s?

13. "The experience of black American soldiers during the Second World War was the main cause of increased pressure for civil rights after 1945." How far do you agree?

Russia

14. How important was the policy of Russification in assisting the Tsarist state to maintain its authority in the years before 1905?

15. Why did the Dumas have so little influence on the Tsarist state between 1905 and 1914?

16. "Nicholas II's fall from power was due mainly to his own weaknesses as a ruler." How far do you accept this explanation for the Revolution of February 1917?

17. How far was the failure of the White armies during the Civil War due to disunity and divided leadership?

[END OF QUESTION PAPER]

[BLANK PAGE]

X044/302

NATIONAL
QUALIFICATIONS
2006

MONDAY, 22 MAY
10.40 AM – 12.05 PM

HISTORY
HIGHER
Paper 2

Answer questions on only **one** Special Topic.

Take particular care to show clearly the Special Topic chosen. On the **front** of the answer book, **in the top right-hand corner**, write the number of the Special Topic.

You are expected to use background knowledge appropriately in answering source-based questions.

Marks may be deducted for bad spelling and bad punctuation, and for writing that is difficult to read.

Some sources have been adapted or translated.

SCOTTISH
QUALIFICATIONS
AUTHORITY

PB X044/302   6/14070

[BLANK PAGE]

OPTION A: MEDIEVAL HISTORY

SPECIAL TOPIC 1: NORMAN CONQUEST AND EXPANSION 1050–1153

Study the sources below and then answer the questions which follow.

Source A: from the Bayeux Tapestry, showing the Battle of Hastings. The wavy line under the infantry and the cavalry represents a hill.

Source B: from *The Anglo-Saxon Chronicle*.

William swore (before the Archbishop would place the crown on his head) that he would rule all his people as well as the best of the kings before him, if they would be loyal to him. All the same he taxed people very severely, and then went in spring [1067] overseas to Normandy, and took with him archbishop Stigand, and Aethelnoth, abbot of Glastonbury, and Edgar and earl Edwin and earl Morcar and earl Waltheof . . . and many other good men from England. And bishop Odo and earl William [of Hereford] stayed behind and built castles far and wide throughout this country, and distressed the wretched folk, and always after that it grew much worse. May the end be good when God wills!

Source C: from the *Ecclesiastical History* of Orderic Vitalis, written *c*. 1114–1141.

When the Norman conquest had brought such grievous burdens upon the English, Bleddyn, king of the Welsh, came to the help of his uncles, bringing a great army of Welshmen with him. After large numbers of the leading men of England and Wales had met together, a general outcry arose against the injustice and tyranny which the Normans and their comrades-in-arms had inflicted on the English.

To meet the danger the king rode to all the remote parts of his kingdom and fortified strategic sites against enemy attacks. For the fortifications called castles by the Normans were scarcely known in the English provinces, and so the English, in spite of their courage and love of fighting, could put up only a weak resistance to their enemies. The king built a castle at Warwick and gave it into the keeping of Henry, son of Roger of Beaumont. After this Edwin, Morcar and their men, unwilling to face the doubtful issue of a battle, and wisely preferring peace to war, sought the king's pardon and obtained it at least in outward appearance. Next the king built Nottingham castle and entrusted it to William Peverel.

Source D: from D. Bates, *William the Conqueror* (1989).

In the event of a Norman summoning an Englishman to defend himself on a serious criminal charge, such as perjury, murder or theft, a concession was made to English legal procedure. The Englishman was allowed to choose between ordeal by hot iron, which was used in England before 1066, or trial by combat, which was not. This admirably sums up William's attitude to the English: on the one hand, the ferocious crushing of all acts of violent resistance in the name of law and order, and on the other, the creation of mechanisms to resolve areas of social difference for those willing to live at peace.

For all the apparent efforts to achieve integration and reconciliation, the historian cannot overlook the fact that the Norman Conquest was a complete catastrophe as far as the English aristocracy was concerned. Many lost their lands and many more chose to emigrate in preference to living under Norman rule.

Source E: from H. R. Loyn, *The Norman Conquest* (1965).

William was, by reputation and in fact, one of the most active monarchs ever to have occupied the throne of England. He nevertheless remained a Norman, Duke William II of Normandy . . . William faced a very difficult political situation in the north of France . . . His main troubles came from inside his own family, especially from his eldest son Robert Curthose. Robert almost ruined the duchy, and it needed the best efforts, first of William Rufus, who held the duchy in pledge for three years when Robert was away on Crusade, and then of Henry I after his victory in 1106, to repair the damage done by their generous, irresponsible elder brother.

[END OF SOURCES FOR SPECIAL TOPIC 1]

SPECIAL TOPIC 1: NORMAN CONQUEST AND EXPANSION 1050–1153

Answer *all* of the following questions.

Marks

1. How fully does **Source A** show the tactics used by Harold and William throughout the Battle of Hastings?
   Use the source and recalled knowledge. **6**

2. How valuable is **Source B** as evidence of William's policy towards the English immediately after the Battle of Hastings?
   In reaching a conclusion you should refer to:
   * *the origin and possible purpose of the source;*
   * *the content of the source;*
   * *recalled knowledge.* **5**

3. To what extent do **Sources B** and **C** agree about the methods which William used to govern England after the conquest?
   Compare the sources overall and in detail. **5**

4. To what extent did William destroy Anglo-Saxon society and government?
   *Use **Sources B**, **C** and **D** and recalled knowledge.* **8**

5. How effectively did Henry I deal with the problems identified in **Source E**?
   Use the source and recalled knowledge. **6**

   (30)

[END OF QUESTIONS ON SPECIAL TOPIC 1]

SPECIAL TOPIC 2: THE CRUSADES 1096–1204

Study the sources below and then answer the questions which follow.

Source A: an Illumination from the thirteenth-century manuscript, "Les Histoires d'Outremer", showing the Crusaders bombarding Nicea with the severed heads of captive Muslim knights.

Source B: from an account of the Battle of Hattin, 1187 by a local Frank, "Ernoul", written soon after 1197.

King Guy and his army left the spring of Saffuriya to go to save Tiberias. As soon as they had left the water behind, Saladin ordered his skirmishers to harass them from morning until midday. The heat was so great that they could not go on to find water. The king and all the other people were spread out and did not know what to do. They could not turn back for the losses would have been too great. He sent to the count of Tripoli, who led the advance guard, to ask advice as to what to do. He sent word that he should pitch his tent and make camp. The king gladly accepted this bad advice. Some people in the army said that if the Christians had gone on to meet the Saracens, Saladin would have been defeated.

As soon as they were encamped, Saladin ordered all his men to collect brushwood, dry grass, stubble and anything else with which they could light fires, and make barriers all round the Christians. They soon did this, and the fires burned vigorously and the smoke from the fires was great. This, together with the heat of the sun, caused them discomfort and great harm. Saladin had commanded caravans of camels loaded with water from the Sea of Tiberias to be brought up and had water pots placed near the camp. The water pots were then emptied in view of the Christians so that they should have still greater anguish through thirst, and their horses too.

Source C: the Massacre of Acre, from the *Itinerarium Peregrinorum et Gesta Regis Ricardi,* a contemporary chronicle of the Third Crusade, based on eye witness accounts.

Saladin had not arranged for the return of the Holy Cross. Instead, he neglected the hostages who were held as security for its return. He hoped that by using the Holy Cross he could gain much greater concessions in negotiation. Saladin meanwhile was sending gifts and messengers to the king, gaining time by false and clever words. He fulfilled none of his promises, but attempted for a long time to keep the king from making up his mind . . .

After the time limit had more than passed, King Richard thought that Saladin had hardened his heart and cared no longer about ransoming the hostages. He assembled a council of the greater men and they decided that they would wait no longer, but that they would behead the captives. They decided, however, to set apart some of the more noble men on the chance that they might be ransomed or exchanged for some other Christian captives.

He ordered that two thousand seven hundred of the vanquished Turkish hostages be led out of the city and decapitated. Without delay his assistants rushed up and quickly carried out the order. They gave heartfelt thanks, since with the approval of divine grace they were taking vengeance in kind for the death of the Christians whom these people had slaughtered.

Source D: from T. Jones and A. Ereira, *Crusade* (1996).

Richard was anxious to get to Jerusalem and he had no intention of hanging around in Acre for the drawn-out process of ransoming prisoners. He had nearly three thousand captured Moslems on his hands. Saladin, in his situation, would have released the prisoners. In fact Saladin had already been heavily criticised by his own people for releasing so many of the prisoners of Hattin and for allowing Tyre to be reinforced with the men he had freed.

Richard agreed with these critics. He therefore took the first opportunity of a hitch in the ransom arrangements to butcher all his prisoners. Some 2700 survivors of the Moslem garrison, with three hundred of their wives and children, were taken outside the city walls in chains and slaughtered in cold blood in the sight of Saladin's army.

Source E: from D. Nicolle, *The Crusades* (2001).

Before the First Crusade, most Western European states had at best a distant relationship with the Muslims of the Eastern Mediterranean. The only exceptions were some Italian merchant republics and the Norman kingdom of Southern Italy and Sicily . . . For the merchants on both sides such links were purely commercial . . . There was surely an element of economic opportunism on the part of some Italian participants in the Crusades.

The economic impact of two centuries of Crusading warfare upon some parts of Europe was considerable. In many other areas however, this impact was negligible. While in countries such as France, Germany and England the need to raise money to finance the Crusades did play some role in the development of government financial systems, it was only in Italy that the economic impact of Crusades was really important. Even here the events of the 12th and 13th centuries were only part of the longer history of the trading relationships between the Italian states and their Islamic neighbours to the south and east.

[END OF SOURCES FOR SPECIAL TOPIC 2]

SPECIAL TOPIC 2: THE CRUSADES 1096–1204

Marks

Answer *all* of the following questions.

1. How useful is **Source A** as evidence of barbaric behaviour by the Crusaders?
   In reaching a conclusion you should refer to:
   * *the origin and possible purpose of the source;*
   * *the content of the source;*
   * *recalled knowledge.*   5

2. How fully does **Source B** describe the events of the Battle of Hattin?
   Use the source and recalled knowledge.   6

3. Compare the explanations for the Massacre of Acre in **Sources C** and **D**.
   Compare the sources overall and in detail.   5

4. How fully do **Sources B**, **C** and **E** describe the crusading ideal?
   *Use **Sources B**, **C** and **E** and recalled knowledge.*   8

5. To what extent do you agree with David Nicolle's view in **Source E** about the economic impact of the Crusades throughout Europe.
   Use the source and recalled knowledge.   6

   (30)

[END OF QUESTIONS ON SPECIAL TOPIC 2]

OPTION B: EARLY MODERN HISTORY

SPECIAL TOPIC 3: SCOTLAND 1689–1715

Study the sources below and then answer the questions which follow.

Source A: from P. W. J. Riley, *The Union of Scotland and England* (1978).

From the parliament of 1703 emerged the Act Anent Peace and War and the Act of Security, both forced on the court by the ill-assorted opposition and both important links in the chain of events leading to the union. The first Act invested in the Scottish parliament for the future, the final decision on Scotland's declaring war. The prospect worried Godolphin but, despite his private protests to the Scottish officers of state, the queen was advised to let it become law. The Act of Security was intended to lay down the conditions under which the next successor to the Scottish throne was to be selected, conditions which would ensure that the choice was free of English influence. For the English the alarming part of the Act was the "communication of trade" clause. By this provision the separation of England and Scotland was envisaged on the death of the queen unless, in the meantime, the Scots had been granted amongst other things, full freedom of trade with England and her colonies.

Source B: from James Hodges, *The Rights and Interests of the Two British Monarchies* (1703).

There is a proposal for a federal union under one Monarch. In it, there shall be no other alteration in the constitutions of either Kingdom, but that each . . . are to retain their National Distinction, to enjoy their particular Liberties, Privileges, and Independence, and to hold their different governments in Church and State, with the laws, customs and rights of the same, as they did before the Union . . . This kind of union is different from that, which some insist upon for uniting the two into one kingdom, one government, one parliament etc under the title of an incorporating union . . .

A federal union is much more agreeable to the real interests of both nations . . . But it is simply impossible to consult the true interests of either nation by an incorporating union, however contrived or qualified.

Source C: from a speech by Seton of Pitmedden in the Scots Parliament, 1706.

There can be no sure guarantee for the observance of the articles of a federal union between two nations, where one is much superior to the other in riches, numbers of people and an extended commerce. Do the advantages of a federal union balance its disadvantages? Will the English accept a federal union, supposing it to be for the true interest of both nations? No federal union between Scotland and England is sufficient to secure the peace of this island, or fortify it against the intrigues and invasions of its foreign enemies. England should not give its trade and protection to this nation till both kingdoms are incorporated into one.

Source D: from Houston and Knox (eds), *The New Penguin History of Scotland* (2001).

The first vote on Article one of the Act, requiring that "the two Kingdoms of England and Scotland shall . . . be united into one Kingdom by the name of Great Britain", resulted in a crown majority of thirty-three, a comfortable but not an entirely reassuring result. The government was especially concerned about the influence of the Church of Scotland, and therefore passed a separate Act guaranteeing its Presbyterian future. This removed a good deal of popular resistance, as well as calming opposition among the Whig-Presbyterian interest in the chamber. Promises to pay off Darien investors from the Equivalent, a large lump sum of £398,085 10s sterling, persuaded Tweeddale's New Party to unite with the court. There is no question that Queensberry used the usual methods of bribery and coercion, including £20,000 sterling from the English treasury, to stiffen the resolve of government supporters who were awaiting arrears of their salaries.

Source E: from a letter written by the earl of Mar to the earl of Leven, 1708.

The Queen called a Cabinet Council last night, where she was pleased to call the dukes of Queensberry and Montrose, the earl of Loudon, Seafield and myself. We gave an account there of what orders the Queen had sent to Scotland, since the news of the invasion . . . It is expected that the Council will seize the horses and arms of those they think disloyal, and will also be giving their advice and instructions for securing the money, in the Mint and Bank, in case of a [hostile] landing . . . It was told to us that since both Houses had advised the Queen to arrest such persons as she had cause to suspect, and are now discussing a Bill for the suspending of Habeas Corpus Acts, it was appropriate that suspected people in Scotland should be arrested.

[END OF SOURCES FOR SPECIAL TOPIC 3]

SPECIAL TOPIC 3: SCOTLAND 1689–1715

Answer *all* of the following questions.

Marks

1. How far does **Source A** explain why relations between Scotland and England were strained in the period 1689 – 1705?
   Use the source and recalled knowledge. 7

2. Compare the attitudes towards Union expressed in **Sources B** and **C**.
   Compare the sources overall and in detail. 5

3. How typical is **Source C** of the opinions of Scottish supporters of Union?
   Use the source and recalled knowledge. 5

4. How fully do **Sources A**, **C**, and **D** explain the reasons for the passing of the Treaty of Union?
   *Use **Sources A, C and D** and recalled knowledge.* 8

5. How valuable is **Source E** as evidence of immediate problems following the Union?
   In reaching a conclusion you should refer to:
   * *the origin and possible purpose of the source;*
   * *the content of the source;*
   * *recalled knowledge.* 5

   (30)

[END OF QUESTIONS ON SPECIAL TOPIC 3]

SPECIAL TOPIC 4: THE ATLANTIC SLAVE TRADE

Study the sources below and then answer the questions which follow.

Source A: from Stephen Fuller, *Remarks on the Resolution of the West India Planters and Merchants* (1789).

In certain vast regions of the African continent, where the arts of rural cultivation are little known, the number of inhabitants grows faster than the means of sustaining them. Humane concerns force the sending of the surplus, as objects of traffic, to more enlightened, or less populous countries. These countries, standing in constant need of their labour, receive them into property, protection and employment.

Source B: from Peter J. Kitson, *Slavery, Abolition and Emancipation: Volume 2—The Abolition Debate* (1999).

The anti-slavery movement was made up of several different perspectives: philosophical, religious, economic, legal and political . . . In Britain many of the leading thinkers were opposed to slavery . . . Adam Smith insisted that freemen would work better than slaves and that slave labour is the most expensive form of labour . . . By the close of the eighteenth century, the slave trade was largely regarded as contrary to religion, nature and justice . . . The contribution of the Friends [Quakers] to anti-slavery opinion was vital. They believed that slavery was against the will of God as revealed in the Old and New Testaments.

Another important factor in the growth of the opposition against the slave trade was the rise in evangelical Christianity in Great Britain in the late eighteenth century, members of which increasingly came to regard slavery as contrary to the law of Christian love. The evangelical Christians combined a belief in a universal humanity with a strong sense of individual guilt as well as a desire to relieve the sufferings of people through good works.

Source C: from a petition to Parliament, from the Archdeaconry of Leicester, quoted in *Gentleman's Magazine LXII* (1792).

As Ministers of that Holy Religion which promotes universal love, we feel bound humbly to protest against a traffic, which is a constant violation of the most essential duties of Christianity. This, if continued under the sanction of the British Legislature, may be expected to bring down upon this country the severest judgement of Heaven.

Source D: from a speech in the House of Commons by Bamber Gasgoyne, 1806.

The attempts to make a popular outcry against this trade were never so conspicuous as in the late election, when the public newspapers teemed with abuse . . . and when promises were required from the different candidates that they would oppose its continuance There never had been any question since that of parliamentary reform in which so much energy had been exerted to raise a popular prejudice . . . in every manufacturing town and borough.

Every measure that invention or skill could devise to create a popular outcry was resorted to on this occasion. The Church, the theatre and the press had laboured to create a prejudice against the Slave Trade.

Source E: from Adrian Hastings, "Abolitionists Black and White", in D. Northrup (ed), *The Atlantic Slave Trade* (2002).

In 1807, the bill for the abolition of the slave trade was passed by the British Parliament, just twenty years after the Abolition Committee was first formed in London. It was, despite the delay (in large part due to the counter-effect of the French Revolution and the war), an impressive achievement.

It was managed by the combination of an efficient "moderate" leadership, at once religious and political, with a nation-wide public opinion produced by a great deal of campaigning. The sustained parliamentary spokesmanship of Wilberforce, personal friend for so many years of the Prime Minister, was invaluable, though the true architects of abolition were Granville Sharp and Thomas Clarkson. A cause which in the early 1780s still seemed eccentric was rendered respectable by the underlying support of the two greatest parliamentarians of the age – Pitt and Fox. It would certainly not have been carried through without very powerful religious convictions at work. It seems hard to deny that it was due to the persevering commitment to the abolitionist cause of quite a small group of men whose separate abilities and positions were knitted together to form a lobby of exceptional effectiveness.

[END OF SOURCES FOR SPECIAL TOPIC 4]

SPECIAL TOPIC 4: THE ATLANTIC SLAVE TRADE

Answer *all* of the following questions.

Marks

1. How typical is the evidence in **Source A** of the arguments used by supporters of the Slave Trade?
   Use the source and recalled knowledge.

   6

2. To what extent does the evidence in **Source C** support **Source B**'s assessment of the reasons for opposition to the Slave Trade?
   Compare the sources overall and in detail.

   4

3. How useful is **Source D** as evidence of the methods used by the abolitionists to promote their cause?
   In reaching a conclusion you should refer to:
   * *the origin and possible purpose of the source;*
   * *the content of the source;*
   * *recalled knowledge.*

   5

4. How fully do **Sources A, B** and **E** identify the issues in the debate over the Slave Trade?
   *Use **Sources A, B** and **E** and recalled knowledge.*

   8

5. How adequate is the explanation given in **Source E** for the eventual abolition of the Slave Trade in 1807?
   Use the source and recalled knowledge.

   7

   (30)

[END OF QUESTIONS ON SPECIAL TOPIC 4]

SPECIAL TOPIC 5: THE AMERICAN REVOLUTION

Study the sources below and then answer the questions which follow.

Source A: from an article by Dr Samuel Johnson, 1774.

No man is a patriot who justifies the ridiculous claims of the Americans, or who tries to deprive the British nation of its natural and lawful authority over its own colonies (those colonies, which were settled under British protection, were constituted by a British charter and have been defended by British arms).

It is absurd to suppose, that by founding a colony, the nation established an independent power. It is equally absurd to think that when emigrants become rich they shall not contribute to their own defence unless they choose to do so and that they shall not be included in the general system of representation.

He that accepts protection, promises obedience. We have always protected the Americans. We may, therefore, subject them to government. . . . The parliament may enact, for America, a law of capital punishment. It may, therefore, establish a method and level of taxation.

Source B: from a letter from Lord Barrington, Secretary at War, to Dartmouth, American Secretary, 24 December 1774.

I do not believe any ministry will ever attempt another internal tax on the North Americans by Act of Parliament. Experience has shown we do not have the strength in that part of the world to levy such taxes, against a universal opinion prevailing there that we have no right to levy them. Many among ourselves, though persuaded of the right, doubt at least the fairness of such taxations; as the Parliament knows little about the state of the colonies and as the members of neither House are to pay any part of the burden they impose.

Source C: from D. Higginbotham, "The War for Independence, to Saratoga", in J. Greene and J.R. Pole (eds), *A Companion to the American Revolution* (2000).

The campaign of 1776 saw Britain take the offensive; but it is hardly accurate to say that she possessed the lion's share of the advantages. Problems of transportation, communication and supply were serious concerns two hundred years ago. So were her lack of sufficient men under arms. Her generals and admirals were competent enough, though little more than that—Generals Gage, Howe and Clinton were too cautious; Burgoyne and Cornwallis were too aggressive. Admiral Howe was hesitant. Clinton called Howe's naval successors "old women" who got along poorly with their army counterparts. The British generals in America, who were Members of Parliament with alliances to rival political factions, also distrusted each other.

Source D: from a British Officer, describing the retreat of Washington's forces from New York, 1776.

As we go forward into the country, the rebels flee before us, and when we come back they always follow us. It's almost impossible to catch them. They will neither fight, nor totally run away, but they keep at such distance that we are always above a day's march from them. They seem to be playing at hide and seek.

Source E: from a letter from Lord Cornwallis to General Clinton, written at Yorktown, October 20, 1781.

Sir, I am ashamed to inform your Excellency that I have been forced to give up the posts of York and Gloucester and to surrender the troops under my command by surrendering on the 19th of this month as prisoners of war to the combined forces of America and France.

I never saw this command at Yorktown in a very favourable light . . . Only the hope of reinforcement or rescue made me attempt its defence. Otherwise I would either have tried to escape to New York by rapid marches from the Gloucester side immediately on the arrival of General Washington's troops at Williamsburgh, or I would, despite the inequality of numbers, have attacked them in the open field . . . But being assured by your Excellency's letters that every possible means would be tried by the navy and army to relieve us, I could not think myself able to attempt either of those desperate measures . . .

[END OF SOURCES FOR SPECIAL TOPIC 5]

SPECIAL TOPIC 5: THE AMERICAN REVOLUTION

Answer *all* of the following questions.

Marks

1. How accurately does **Source A** identify the issues that led to the colonial challenge to British control in America?
   Use the source and recalled knowledge.

   7

2. Compare the views expressed in **Sources A** and **B** on the question of taxing America.
   Compare the sources overall and in detail.

   5

3. How adequately does **Source C** explain the problems faced by Britain after the outbreak of war in America?
   Use the source and recalled knowledge.

   6

4. How useful is **Source D** as evidence of the tactics used by colonial troops in the war?
   In reaching a conclusion you should refer to:
   * *the origin and possible purpose of the source;*
   * *the content of the source;*
   * *recalled knowledge.*

   4

5. How fully do **Sources C**, **D** and **E** explain the reasons for colonial victory in the war?
   *Use **Sources C**, **D** and **E** and recalled knowledge.*

   8

   (30)

[END OF QUESTIONS ON SPECIAL TOPIC 5]

OPTION C: LATER MODERN HISTORY

SPECIAL TOPIC 6: PATTERNS OF MIGRATION: SCOTLAND 1830s–1930s

Study the sources below and then answer the questions which follow.

Source A: from *Glasgow Past and Present*, 23 July 1849.

There are not less than 50,000 Irish people, or of Irish descent, in Glasgow. A very small proportion of these, as compared with Catholics, are Orangemen or Protestants. In 1846, according to information kindly supplied by the Bishop, no fewer than 3,000 children were baptised in the various Catholic places of worship in the city.

A gentleman, still living, remembers when the first Irishman planted himself down in Gorbals, where he was considered as much a curiosity for a time as if he had been a tattooed New Zealander. At the present moment the principal parts of Gorbals, in Main Street and its vicinity, are almost entirely in the possession of these invaders who, however, are generally an orderly and hard working class of people. They give little trouble to the police, as compared with their countrymen in other parts of the city. Further, Mr. R. Lindsay remembers when the first Irishman wriggled himself into the locality of Fiddlers' Close and the man was tolerated by the Scotch inhabitants by reason of his agreeing to keep the close clean.

Source B: from R. Swift and S. Gilley (eds), *The Irish in the Victorian City* (1985).

The Irish were thoroughly disliked and feared for the problems which they brought in their wake. Not the least of these was disease. Typhus was sometimes called "famine disease" or "Irish fever", and its association with the Irish hastened the emergence of distinct ghettoes or "Little Irelands". Some of the Irish rejected the housing standards of the native poor and were condemned for their unhygienic habits. The expectations of most immigrants were set by what was commonplace in Ireland, but Ireland was much poorer than Britain. The prominence of the Irish in the crime statistics was another cause of complaint, although their offences were mostly of a minor nature—drunkenness, petty theft and offences against the person. There were numerous complaints about the Irish share of poor relief in areas of heavy immigration . . . Indeed, many viewed the arrival of the Irish as a social disaster and residential segregation set them apart from the local population.

Source C: from the *Aberdeen Herald*, 4 December 1852.

The farm workers were honest, plain, hard-working men, who looked forward to the day when they or their sons would be able to get larger and larger farms as their honest savings increased. These men, in many cases, have been obliged, along with their families, to leave for our towns in order to get employment, or have emigrated to countries where their skill and hard work will be more highly appreciated. A farm servant, who may have saved fifty or sixty pounds, can not even get a small farm upon which he might invest his small sum of money. His only refuge is a foreign land; and thus it is that our very best agricultural labourers are driven from this country by the foolishness of "penny wise and pound foolish" landowners . . . It is clear that the cold and damp bothy will not persuade our young ploughmen to remain at home and give up their chance of comfort, if not wealth, in America or Australia.

Source D: from a statement by George Wood, a Scottish emigrant to Canada, 1842.

I emigrated to this country with my wife and five children seven years ago. We all have enjoyed good health as the climate in this part of the country is remarkably healthy. I consider that the change by emigrating here is to my advantage, and that of my family. I am quite in a different situation now in this country as regards acquired property from what I would have been in had I remained in Scotland. By adopting this country as the future home of myself and family, I am now a master, where I could never well expect otherwise than to see myself and my family as servants in the old country. The ease of acquiring property here is great, and any man, single or married, of sober, economical, hardworking and persevering habits is sure to do well.

Source E: from "Scotland's Story", a Scottish Television Production (1988).

The religious divide lasted well into the twentieth century. It was hard for a Catholic to make progress up the social and career ladder in certain jobs. Few Catholics obtained employment in the shipyards; the medical profession (not openly) did not encourage doctors from certain schools to enter some areas of medicine. Irish Catholics thus found things more difficult. It is fair to say however, that working class people of all faiths found progress in certain professions more difficult than middle class people.

[*END OF SOURCES FOR SPECIAL TOPIC 6*]

SPECIAL TOPIC 6: PATTERNS OF MIGRATION: SCOTLAND 1830s–1930s

Answer *all* of the following questions.   *Marks*

1. To what extent does **Source A** reflect Scottish attitudes towards Irish immigrants in the mid-nineteenth century?
   Use the source and recalled knowledge.   **6**

2. How far does the evidence in **Source A** support the views of the historian in **Source B** about the impact of Irish immigration on life in Scotland?
   Compare the sources overall and in detail.   **5**

3. How useful is **Source C** as evidence of the reasons for Scottish emigration during the period from the 1830s to the 1930s?
   In reaching a conclusion you should refer to:
   * *the origin and possible purpose of the source;*
   * *the content of the source;*
   * *recalled knowledge.*   **5**

4. How typical were the experiences of George Wood (**Source D**) of Scottish emigrants between the 1830s and 1930s?
   Use the source and recalled knowledge.   **6**

5. How successful were immigrant groups in being accepted as part of Scottish society between the 1830s and 1930s?
   *Use **Sources A, B** and **E** and recalled knowledge.*   **8**

                                                                                                                    (30)

[*END OF QUESTIONS ON SPECIAL TOPIC 6*]

SPECIAL TOPIC 7: APPEASEMENT AND THE ROAD TO WAR, TO 1939

Study the sources below and then answer the questions which follow.

Source A: from a letter written by a young American member of the International Brigade, 1938.

Somewhere in Spain

In the event of my death, will the finder please mail this letter to my mother?

Dear Mom

In Spain there are countless thousands of mothers like yourself who never had a fair chance in life. One day the Spanish people did something about that. They got together and elected a government that really gave some meaning to their lives. But it didn't work out the way the poor people expected. A group of bullies decided to crush and wipe out this wonderful thing the poor people had accomplished and drive them back to the old way of life.

Don't let anyone mislead you, Mom, by telling you that all this had something to do with Communism. The Hitlers and Mussolinis of this world are killing Spanish people who don't know the difference between Communism and rheumatism. And it's not to set up some Communist government, either. The only thing the Communists did here was to show the people how to fight and win what is rightfully theirs.

I was always proud and grateful that you were my Mom.

Your son

Will

Source B: from a speech by Winston Churchill in the House of Commons, 19 July 1937.

It is well known that ordinary guarantees for safety and order had largely lapsed in Spain, that it was not safe for people to go out at night over large areas, that murders and outrages were rife. Constitutional parliamentary government was being used . . . to cover the swift, stealthy and deadly advance of the extreme Communist or anarchist factions. They saw, according to the regular programme of Communist revolutions, the means by which they could obtain power. It was when confronted with a situation like that, that this violent explosion [the Civil War] took place in Spain.

Source C: from Andrew Boxer, *Appeasement* (1998).

The record of British foreign policy in this period [1930–1937] looks grim. The failure to resist aggression in Abyssinia encouraged the dictators and destroyed the credibility of the League of Nations. Italy was alienated as a potential ally. Aggression in Spain was ignored. Britain accepted Hitler's destruction of the military clauses of the Treaty of Versailles without gaining much in return. Significant differences developed between Britain and France about how to handle the dictators.

Source D: from a speech by Viscount Astor in Parliament, 16 March 1938.

By our failure to settle certain questions in the past we must bear a certain measure of responsibility for the way in which things have happened. By the peace treaties the Austrian-Hungarian Empire was broken up and its population divided. As a result we had economic distress in Austria. The Schuschnigg government was felt to be a weak government and there was a tendency for people to drift either to Nazis or Communists.

At present I do not believe that any government, whether democratic or totalitarian, can face the possibility of a world war. Now the long range bomber means the civilian population of Germany will suffer as much as the civilian population elsewhere. It is likely that another war will be followed by revolution and the growth of Communism. Therefore I do not think any country will consider war. I cannot help thinking the way is still open to negotiation which will lead to some all round settlement. At all events it is worth exploring. There are only two alternatives I can see. One is to talk; the other is to a blind drift to war.

Source E: the cover of the Italian magazine, *Illustrazione del Popolo*, 9-15 October 1938.

1° OTTOBRE 1938: UNA DATA STORICA.
Le truppe liberatrici entrano nelle terre sudetiche restituite alla Germania
in virtù del Protocollo di Monaco.

The caption reads, " 1st October 1938: a historic date. The liberating troops enter the Sudetenland restored to Germany through the Munich agreement".

[END OF SOURCES FOR SPECIAL TOPIC 7]

SPECIAL TOPIC 7: APPEASEMENT AND THE ROAD TO WAR, TO 1939

Answer *all* of the following questions.   *Marks*

1. How valuable is **Source A** as evidence of the motives of members of the International Brigade during the Spanish Civil War?
    In reaching a conclusion you should refer to:
    *   *the origin and possible purpose of the source;*
    *   *the content of the source;*
    *   *recalled knowledge.*   5

2. Compare the views about the Spanish Civil War expressed in **Sources A** and **B**.
    Compare the sources overall and in detail.   5

3. How far to do you agree with **Source C**'s assessment of British foreign policy up to 1937?
    Use the source and recalled knowledge.   6

4. How typical is **Source E** of international reactions to the Munich agreement?
    Use the source and recalled knowledge.   6

5. How fully do **Sources A**, **D** and **E** illustrate attitudes towards appeasement during the late 1930s?
    *Use Sources **A**, **D** and **E** and recalled knowledge.*   8

[END OF QUESTIONS ON SPECIAL TOPIC 7]   **(30)**

SPECIAL TOPIC 8: THE ORIGINS AND DEVELOPMENT OF THE COLD WAR 1945–1985

Study the sources below and then answer the questions which follow.

Source A: from a report by Simon Bourgin, an American journalist in Budapest, 5 July 1956.

The events that started in Moscow with the de-Stalinisation program have more than ever begun to have some kind of influence in Hungary—things are now moving at a pace where the results cannot be predicted . . .

On 27th June, I attended a meeting of the Petofi Club, for writers and authors. There were about 2000 people in the audience, about a third of them army officers . . .

One of the speakers was a young lady from the University of Budapest. In her speech she stated that the people in the regime had lost touch with the rank and file of the Party, and with the common people altogether. They bought their clothes and food out of special shops in Budapest, they lived in expensive five-room villas. They had forgotten that most people were crowded one family to a room, and that a lot of people in Budapest did not have enough to eat. She finished by saying that there absolutely had to be a change in Party leadership.

Source B: from W.R. Keylor, *The Twentieth Century World* (4th edn., 2001).

The prospect of a politically independent and militarily neutral Hungary was evidently too much for the Soviet leadership to accept. It would establish a dangerous precedent that, if followed by the other East European states, could only bring about the disintegration of the buffer zone between Russia and the West, which Russia had established after the collapse of Hitler's Reich. The "liberation" of the Soviet East European Empire and the "rollback" of Communist power to the Russian frontier suddenly seemed imminent, not because of American pressure, but because of the explosion of unrestrained nationalism in Hungary.

On 4 November 1956, the Russian Army returned in force to Budapest. The Nagy government was forcibly replaced by a puppet government under Janos Kadar, whose authority rested entirely on the presence of Soviet troops.

Source C: from A. Dobson and S. Marsh, *US Foreign Policy since 1945* (2001).

After the Americans discovered the Russian missiles in Cuba, there was never any argument about the fact that they had to go. They could not stay for three basic reasons . . .

First, they would have had a psychological impact which would have been very damaging politically . . . It was bad enough having a communist state in the Western hemisphere—one with nucelar weapons was just not acceptable. It would have altered the perceptions of the relative standing of the USA and the Soviet Union in the Cold War and, as Kennedy commented, perceptions contribute to reality.

Second, the missiles would have strengthened the Soviet Union's strike capability and cut down the warning time.

Third, it might have encouraged the Russians to take other chances, risking unintentional nuclear war.

Source D: from a policy Memorandum by Dean Rusk (Secretary of State) and Robert McNamara (Secretary of Defence) to President Kennedy, 1961.

The deteriorating situation in South Vietnam requires the attention of the United States. The loss of South Vietnam to communism would involve the transfer of a nation of 20 million people from the free world to the Communist bloc . . . We would have to face the near certainty that the rest of Southeast Asia would move closer to communism . . .

The United States should commit itself to the clear objective of preventing the fall of South Vietnam to communism . . . We must try to put the government of South Vietnam into a position to win its own war against the communist guerrillas. We should also be prepared to introduce United States combat forces if that should become necessary for success . . . It may also be necessary for United States forces to strike at the source of the aggression in North Vietnam.

Source E: from a speech by Senator Mike Mansfield, 1962.

If our present level of support for South Vietnam does not work, it is difficult to conceive of alternatives, with the possible exception of a truly massive commitment of American military personnel—in short, going to war ourselves against the guerrillas.

That is an alternative which I most emphatically do not recommend. On the contrary, it seems to me most essential that we make it crystal clear to South Vietnam that, while we will go to great lengths to help, the primary responsibility rests with the Vietnamese. It is their country, their future which is most at stake, not ours. To ignore that reality will not only be immensely costly in terms of American lives and resources, but it may also draw us into a conflict which we cannot win.

[END OF SOURCES FOR SPECIAL TOPIC 8]

SPECIAL TOPIC 8: THE ORIGINS AND DEVELOPMENT OF THE COLD WAR 1945–1985

Answer *all* of the following questions.

Marks

1. How valuable is **Source A** as evidence of the growth of discontent in Hungary in 1956?
   In reaching a conclusion you should refer to:
   • *the origin and possible purpose of the source;*
   • *the content of the source;*
   • *recalled knowledge.*

   5

2. How fully does **Source B** explain the reasons for the actions taken by the USSR in Hungary in 1956?
   Use the source and recalled knowledge.

   6

3. To what extent do the views expressed in **Source C** explain American concerns and actions over Cuba in 1962?
   Use the source and recalled knowledge.

   6

4. Compare the views in **Sources D** and **E** on the case for American military involvement in Vietnam.
   Compare the sources overall and in detail.

   5

5. How adequately do **Sources B**, **C** and **D** explain the reasons for tension between the Superpowers up to the mid-1960s?
   *Use **Sources B**, **C** and **D** and recalled knowledge.*

   8

   (30)

[END OF QUESTIONS ON SPECIAL TOPIC 8]

SPECIAL TOPIC 9: IRELAND 1900–1985: A DIVIDED IDENTITY

Study the sources below and then answer the questions which follow.

Source A: from a speech by John Redmond in the House of Commons, 15 September 1914.

For the first time . . . Ireland in this war feels her interests are precisely the same as yours. She feels that British democracy has kept faith with her . . . The men of Ireland will spring to your aid in this war.

I have promised publicly, on hundreds of platforms during the last few years, that when the rights of Ireland were accepted by the democracy of England, then Ireland would become the strongest arm in the defence of the Empire.

I would feel personally dishonoured if I did not say to my fellow-countrymen that it is their duty, and should be their honour, to take their place in the firing line in this contest.

Source B: from an article by Arthur Griffith in *Sinn Féin* newspaper, 8 August 1914.

Ireland is not at war with Germany. She has no quarrel with any Continental power. England is at war with Germany, and Mr. Redmond has offered England the services of the Irish Volunteers to "defend Ireland". What has Ireland to defend, and whom has she to defend it against?

There is no European power waging war against the people of Ireland. There are two European powers at war with the people who dominate Ireland from Dublin Castle.

Our duty is not in doubt. We are Irish Nationalists and the only duty we can have is to stand for Ireland's interests, irrespective of the interests of England or Germany or any other foreign country.

Source C: from an article in the *Irish Times*, 1 May 1916.

It is believed that most of the leaders of the Rising are dead or captured. So ends the criminal adventure of the men who declared that they were "striking in full confidence of victory" and that they would be supported by "gallant allies in Europe".

The gallant allies' only gift to them was an Irish renegade [Roger Casement]. Ireland has been saved from shame and ruin, and the whole Empire from a serious danger. Where our politicians failed, the British army has won the day.

Treason must be rooted out of Ireland once and for all. The violence and bloodshed of the past week must be finished with a severity which will make any repetition of them impossible for generations to come.

Source D: from F.S.L. Lyons, "The Rising and After", in W.E. Vaughan (ed.), *A New History of Ireland* (1996).

The initial unpopularity of the Rising should have been regarded by the British government as a priceless asset. This indeed it would have been, if it had not been squandered in part, by the policy of internment. This herded innocent men and women into camps alongside dedicated revolutionaries, and exposed them to a process of indoctrination of which the full consequences were only to be seen in the years that lay ahead.

In addition, the asset of public hostility to the Rising was squandered by the policy adopted towards its leaders. Not only were they tried by secret courts martial, but the executions were spun out over ten days. This was sufficient time for feelings of compassion for the victims and anger against the authorities to replace the original public condemnation of the Rising.

Source E: from J. Smith, *Britain and Ireland: From Home Rule to Independence* (2000).

The Anglo-Irish War was little more than a dirty war between hard men and gangsters on both sides—men who were incapable of adjusting to the normalities of peace, after the bloodletting of the Great War. It was a conflict characterised by spies and informers, of midnight executions, and a bullet in the back of the head—of guilt by association or family or religion, and of widespread intimidation of ordinary people by both sides.

Yet, it was a war neither side could win. As the reality of this sunk in by the summer of 1921, the British moved haltingly towards truce, which was formally agreed on 11 July, and opened the way to more formal peace negotiations.

[END OF SOURCES FOR SPECIAL TOPIC 9]

SPECIAL TOPIC 9: IRELAND 1900–1985: A DIVIDED IDENTITY

Answer *all* of the following questions.

Marks

1. How reliable is **Source A** as evidence of Irish attitudes towards supporting Britain in the First World War?
    In reaching a conclusion you should refer to:
    *   *the origin and possible purpose of the source;*
    *   *the content of the source;*
    *   *recalled knowledge.*   5

2. Compare the attitudes in **Sources A** and **B** on Irish support for Britain in the First World War.
    Compare the sources overall and in detail.   5

3. How fully does **Source C** illustrate Irish reactions to the Easter Rising?
    Use the source and recalled knowledge.   6

4. To what extent does **Source D** explain the effects of the Easter Rising on Ireland up to 1921?
    Use the source and recalled knowledge.   6

5. Why was it so difficult to achieve a peaceful settlement in Ireland in the period after 1914?
    *Use **Sources B**, **D** and **E** and recalled knowledge.*   8

                                                                                                               (30)

[END OF QUESTIONS ON SPECIAL TOPIC 9]

[END OF QUESTION PAPER]

[BLANK PAGE]

Acknowledgements

Leckie & Leckie is grateful to the copyright holders, as credited, for permission to use their material:

2003
The Evening Standard/Atlantic Syndication for a cartoon (p 16).

2004
Extract from *The Norman Conquest and its Effect on the Economy* by R. Welldon Finn, published by Longman. Reproduced by permission of David Higham Associates (p 5);
A cartoon from the *News of the World* 25 September 1938 © NI Syndication, London (p 19);

2005
Eltis, David & Walvin, James, *The Abolition of the Atlantic Slave Trade: Origins & Effects in Europe, Africa and the Americas*. Published 1981 and reprinted by permission of The University of Wisconsin Press (p 10);
Illustrated London News Picture Library for a drawing (p 16);
Punch for a cartoon from 1914 (p 20);

2006
Extract from Essential Histories # 1, The Crusades, by David Nicolle, © Osprey Publishing, www.ospreypublishing.com (p 7).

The following companies/individuals have very generously given permission to reproduce their copyright material free of charge:

2003
Extract from *Conquest and Colonisation* by Brian Golding. Reproduced with permission of Palgrave Macmillan (p 4);
Cambridge University Press for an extract from *The Industrial Revolution in Scotland*, by Christopher A. Whately 1997 (p 5);
Boydell & Brewer Ltd for an extract from *The Normans and the Norman Conquest* by R.A. Brown (p 5);
Saqi Books for an extract from *The Crusade Through Arab Eyes* by A. Maalouf (p 6);
Extract from *The Crusades* by Terry Jones and Alan Ereira reproduced with the permission of BBC Worldwide Limited. Copyright © Fegg Features Limited and Alan Ereira 1994 (p 7);
Birlinn Limited for an extract from *Scotland's Relations with England* by W Ferguson (p 8);
Extract from *The Scottish Nation 1900–2000* by T.M. Devine (Allen Lane The Penguin Press, 1999) copyright © T.M. Devine, 1999 (p 9);
Liverpool University Press for an extract from *The Atlantic Slave Trade and Black Africa* by P.E.H. Hair (p 10);
Hodder & Stoughton for an extract from *Crisis of Empire: Great Britain and the American Colonies 1754-1783* by I.R. Christie (p 12);
Newsquest Media Group for an extract from *The Glasgow Herald* from the 15th March 1929 (p 14);
Oxford University Press, Melbourne for an extract from *The Australian Legend* by Russell Ward (p 15);
The People's Press Printing Society Ltd for an extract from *The Morning Star* (p 16);
Extract from *Europe and the World* by Donald Lindsey. Reprinted by permission of Oxford University Press (p 17);
Extract from *The Rise to Globalism* by Stephen E Ambrose 1997, The Penguin Group USA (p 18);
Extract from 'From Parnell to Pearse' by D.M. McCartney, taken from *The Course of Irish History* by T.W. Moody and F.X. Martin. © Radio Telefis Éireann 1967, 1984, 1994, 2001. Reprinted by kind permission of Mercier Press, Ireland (p 20);

2004
Tempus Publishing Ltd for an extract and two photographs from *The Normans* by Trevor Rowley (pp 4 & 5);
Saqi Books for an extract from *The Crusades Through Arab Eyes* by A. Maalouf (p 8);
Random House for an extract from *The Jacobite Risings in Britain 1689–1746* by Bruce Lenman (p 11);
Pickering & Chatto for an extract from *Slavery, Abolition and Emancipation: Volume 2 The Abolition Debate* by Peter J. Kitson (p 12);
Professor Tom Devine for an extract from *The Herald* (p 16);
Random House for an extract from *Scotland: A New History* by M. Lynch (p 16);
Newsquest for two letters from *The Glasgow Herald* 17th and 18th March 1936 (p 18);
Sutton Publishing for an extract from *The Age of Appeasement: the Evolution of British Foreign Policy in the 1930s* by Peijian Shen (p 19);
Extract from *Memories* by Andrei Gromyko published by Hutchinson. Used by permission of The Random House Group Limited (p 21);
Routledge for an extract from *US Foreign Policy since 1945* by A. Dobson & S. Marsh (p 22);
The Irish Independent for a letter from 17 September 1914 (p 24);
Pearson Education Ltd for an extract from *Britain and Ireland: From Home Rule to Independence* by Jeremy Smith (p 24);

2005

Taylor & Francis Group plc for an extract from *The Medieval Foundations of England* by G. O. Sayles (p 4);

Extract from *The Debate on the Norman Conquest* by M. Chibnall, published by Manchester University Press (p 4);

The Athlone Press for an extract from *The First Crusade and the Idea of Crusading* by Jonathan Riley-Smith (p 6);

Palgrave Macmillan for an extract from *The Invention of the Crusades* by Christopher Tyerman (p 7);

John Donald Publishers (Birlinn) Ltd for an extract from *Andrew Fletcher and the Treaty of the Union* by P.H. Scott (p 8);

Hodder & Stoughton for an extract from *Lordship to Patronage* by Rosalind Mitchison (p 8);

Image of a medallion reproduced courtesy of the Wedgwood Museum Trust, Barlaston, Staffordshire (p 10);

Pickering & Chatto for an extract from *Slavery, Abolition and Emancipation: Volume 2 – The Abolition Debate* by Peter J. Kitson (p10);

University of Wales Press for an extract from *Revolution in America* by Peter D.G. Thomas (p 12);

Extract from *The American Revolution, A People's History* by Ray Raphael, published by Profile Books Limited (p 12);

Extract from *People and Society in Scotland Vol. II, 1830-1914* edited by W. Hamish Fraser and R. J. Morris (p 14);

Routledge for an extract from *The Irish in Britain* by J.A. Jackson (p 14);

Extract from *The Dark Valley* by Piers Brendon, published by Secker & Warburg. Reprinted by permission of The Random House Group (p 17);

Rogers, Coleridge & White Ltd for an extract from *The Green Flag* by Robert Kee (p 18);

2006

Detail from the Bayeux Tapestry reproduced by special permission of the City of Bayeux (p 4);

Tempus Publishing Ltd for an extract from *William the Conqueror* by D. Bates (p 5);

Bibliotheque nationale de France for an Illumination from *Les Histoiries d'Outremer* (p 6);

BBC Worldwide for an extract from *The Crusades* by Terry Jones and Alan Ereira (p 7);

Extract from *The Union of Scotland and England* P. W. J. Riley, published by Manchester University Press (p 8);

Extract from *The New Penguin History of Scotland* edited by Houston and Knox, 2001. Reproduced by permission of Penguin Books Ltd. (p 8);

Houghton Mifflin Company for an extract from 'Abolitionists Black and White' by Adrian Hastings, taken from *The Atlantic Slave Trade* edited by D. Northrup (p 11);

Taylor & Francis Group Ltd for an extract from *The Irish in the Victorian City* edited by R. Swift and S. Gilley (p 14);

Scottish Television for an extract from *Scotland's Story* (p 15);

Extract from *Appeasement* by Andrew Boxer. Reprinted by permission of HarperCollins Publishers Ltd © Andrew Boxer 1998 (p 16);

Curtis Brown for an extract from a speech in The House of Commons by Winston Churchill (p 16);

Her Majesty's Stationary Office for extracts from a speech by Viscount Astor (p 16) and a speech by John Redmond (p 20) © Crown copyright;

Extract from 'The Rising and After' by F.S.L. Lyons, taken from *A New History of Ireland*, edited by W.E. Vaughan. Reproduced by permission of Oxford University Press (p 20);

Pearson Education for an extract from *Britain and Ireland: From Home Rule to Independence* by Jeremy Smith (p 21).